# NEW

# CUTTING EDGE

## INTERMEDIATE

## WORKBOOK

jane comyns carr    frances eales

Longman

# CONTENTS

## Grammar terms

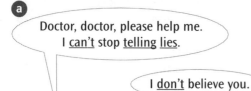

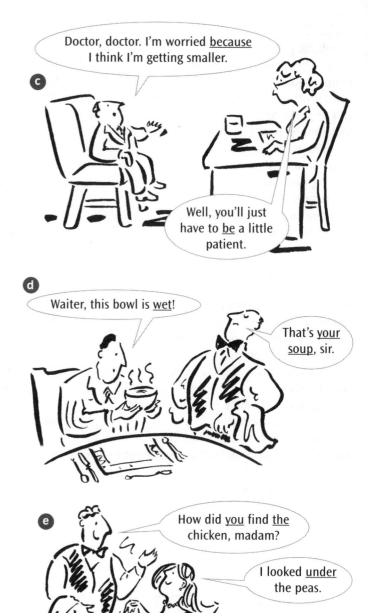

**1** Match the underlined words from the jokes above to the grammar terms.

a  a countable noun _lies_

b  an uncountable noun _____

c  an adjective _____

d  a preposition _____

e  an adverb _____

f  the base form of the verb _____

g  the *-ing* form of the verb _____

h  an auxiliary verb _____

i  a modal auxiliary verb _____

j  a definite article _____

k  an indefinite article _____

l  a pronoun _____

m  a possessive adjective _____

n  a conjunction _____

4

# Using a dictionary

**2** A dictionary can be very useful to find the grammar of a word. Look at these two extracts from the *Longman Active Study Dictionary* and complete the gaps below.

> **Abbreviations**
>
> | | | | |
> |---|---|---|---|
> | *adj* | adjective | *prep* | preposition |
> | *adv* | adverb | *pron* | pronoun |
> | *v* | (verb) | *n* | noun |

> **en•joy** /ɪnˈdʒɔɪ/ (v)[T] to get pleasure from something: *Did you enjoy the movie?* **enjoy doing sth** *My wife really enjoys playing golf.*
>
> **en•joy•ment** *n* [U] *We hope the bad weather didn't spoil your enjoyment.*
>
> **en•joy•a•ble** /ɪnˈdʒɔɪəbəl/ *adj* giving you pleasure: *We all had an enjoyable afternoon.*

> **train²** /treɪn/ *v* [T] to teach someone how to do something, especially the practical skills they need to do a job: *Staff are trained in how to deal with difficult customers.*
>
> **train•ee** /ˌtreɪˈniː/ *n* [C] someone who is being trained for a job: *a trainee teacher*
>
> **train•er** /ˈtreɪnə/ *n* [C] someone whose job is to train people how to do something
>
> **train•ing** /ˈtreɪnɪŋ/ *n* [U] when someone is taught the skills they need to do something: *a training course*

a enjoy is ___*a verb*___

b enjoyment is _____

c enjoyable is _____

d train is _____

e trainee is _____

f trainer is _____

g training is _____

**LONGMAN Active Study Dictionary**

**NOW WITH INTEGRATED THESAURUS**

colour photographs

Longman

**NEW EDITION**

**3** Complete the sentences with the words from the dictionary extracts in exercise 2.

a Where did Jenny ___*train*___ to be a ski instructor?

b My father gets a lot of _____ from his garden.

c I really _____ spending time on my own.

d How much football _____ do you do every day?

e The course was really _____ . I recommend it.

f Patricia's only a _____ chef, but her cooking is fantastic!

g Our _____ wants us to finish our project this week.

## Making questions
### Word order

**1** **a** Put the words in order to make questions.

1 today / you / How / feeling / are

_How are you feeling today?_

2 did / start / Where / your / journey / you

_____ ?

3 need / carrier bag / a / you / Do

_____ ?

4 a / got / the / Has / balcony / room

_____ ?

5 we / practising / were / yesterday / What

_____ ?

6 the / education / are / plans / government's / What / for

_____

_____ ?

7 all / take / the / Did / antibiotics / you

_____ ?

8 suitcase / you / this / yourself / Did / pack

_____ ?

9 served / is / time / What / breakfast

_____ ?

10 number / Have / the / got / six / you / to / answer

_____ ?

11 anything / Are / in / you / for / particular / looking

_____ ?

12 about / did / the / Finance Minister / tax cuts / What / say

_____

_____ ?

**b** Who would ask each question? Write the numbers of the questions in the boxes below.

1 ☐ ☐ a teacher to a student

2 ☐ ☐ a journalist to a politician

3 ☐ ☐ a customs official to a traveller

4 ☐ ☐ a shop assistant to a customer

5 [1] ☐ a doctor to a patient

6 ☐ ☐ a guest to a hotel receptionist

## *be*, *have* and *do* in questions

**2** Stefano is asking his friend Pietro about his new girlfriend. Complete his questions with the correct form of *be*, *have* or *do*.

STEFANO:  What (a) <u>'s</u> your girlfriend's name?

PIETRO:  Masako.

STEFANO:  (b) _____ that a Japanese name?

PIETRO:  Yes, that's right.

STEFANO:  Which part of Japan (c) _____ she come from?

PIETRO:  Osaka.

STEFANO:  Uh-huh ... so (d) _____ you speak Japanese?

PIETRO:  No. 'Hello' and 'thank you', but that's it!

STEFANO:  Oh, right. (e) _____ she doing that English course with you last month?

PIETRO:  No, her English is much better than mine.

STEFANO:  Well, how (f) _____ you meet her, then?

PIETRO:  At the bus stop – she lives near me.

STEFANO:  I see. (g) _____ she got her own flat here?

PIETRO:  Well, it's her parents' flat.

STEFANO:  Oh. (h) _____ they living here, too?

PIETRO:  Some of the time, yes.

## Short answers

**3** **a** Match the questions and short answers.

1  [g]  Do you like our new teacher?
2  [ ]  Have you got the time?
3  [ ]  Is it cold outside today?
4  [ ]  Did you have a good holiday?
5  [ ]  Was there a lot of traffic on the roads this morning?
6  [ ]  Are your neighbours nice?
7  [ ]  Were you at the football match on Saturday?
8  [ ]  Has your brother got a girlfriend?
9  [ ]  Does it take long to do this exercise?
10 [ ]  Was the film good?

a  Yes, they are.        f  No, it isn't.
b  No, he hasn't.        g  Yes, I do.
c  Yes, I did.           h  No, it doesn't.
d  Yes, I was.           i  Yes, there was.
e  No, it wasn't.        j  No, I haven't.

**b** 🔊 **T1.1** Listen to the questions and answers. Notice that the auxiliaries *do/does*, *has/have*, *is/are* and *was/were* are weak in the question, but strong in the short answer.

/də/
Do you like our new teacher?

/du/
Yes, I do.

**c** Listen again and repeat the questions and answers, paying attention to the strong and weak sounds.

**4** Look at the long answers. Write the question and then the short answer for each one.

a  No, I'm not married.
   <u>Are you married</u> ?
   <u>No, I'm not</u> .

b  Yes, I live with my family.
   _____ ?
   _____ .

c  No, we don't live in an apartment.
   _____ ?
   _____ .

d  No, we didn't live in the same place when I was young.
   _____
   _____ ?
   _____ .

e  No, my grandparents aren't alive.
   _____ ?
   _____ .

f  No, I haven't got a car.
   _____ ?
   _____ .

g  Yes, I can understand English well.
   _____ ?
   _____ .

h  No, my English teacher doesn't speak my language.
   _____
   _____ ?
   _____ .

## Question tags

> **He's got** her phone number, **hasn't he?**
>   +                         −
>
> **It isn't** very warm today, **is it?**
>   −                        +
>
> Notice:
> 1  **You take** sugar in your coffee, **don't you?**
>    no auxiliary                auxiliary *do*
> 2  **I'm** really early, **aren't I?**
>                    ~~amn't I?~~

*LOOK!*

**5**  **a**  Complete the sentences with a question tag.

**1** TWO FRIENDS ARE SHOPPING.

a  Ooh, it's cold today, _isn't it_____ ?

b  That coat costs a lot, _____ ?

c  They've got some nice clothes here, _____ ?

d  These jeans are too short, _____ ?

e  There aren't many sales assistants, _____ ?

**2** MRS HALLIDAY IS TALKING TO LIESBETH, WHO HAS COME TO STAY FOR SIX MONTHS AND HELP WITH THE CHILDREN.

a  You're from Amsterdam, _____ ?

b  You speak French, _____ ?

c  You've got two little brothers, _____ ?

d  You don't smoke, _____ ?

e  You can drive, _____ ?

**b**  **T1.2**  Listen to the statements and add the correct question tag.

> **You hear:**
> Ooh, it's cold today, …

> **You say:**
> *Ooh, it's cold today, isn't it?*

## Classroom questions

**6**  Correct the questions.

a  How to pronounce 'b-u-s-i-n-e-s-s'?

  _How do you pronounce 'b-u-s-i-n-e-s-s'_____ ?

b  Can you writing 'customer' on the board, please?

  _____ ?

c  What's English word for this?

  _____ ?

d  Which page we are on?

  _____ ?

e  Have anybody got a spare pen?

  _____ ?

f  Can you say again that, please?

  _____ ?

g  What are tonight's homework?

  _____ ?

h  How you spell 'journey'?

  _____ ?

i  What means 'colleague'?

  _____ ?

## Vocabulary
### How you spend your time

**7**  Complete the sentences with the correct preposition. In one sentence, no preposition is necessary.

a  I've never been interested ___in___ football.

b  My flatmate spends a lot of time _____ the Internet.

c  My parents don't have much time _____ relaxing and doing nothing.

d  My sister and her friends spend too much time chatting _____ the phone.

e  I really love hanging out _____ my friends at the weekend.

f  My colleagues spend a lot of time texting _____ their friends at work.

g  My brother's quite good _____ cooking.

h  My grandmother doesn't know anything _____ computer games.

# Vocabulary booster
## Hobbies

8 a Find the following things in the word square.
(The words go across or down.)

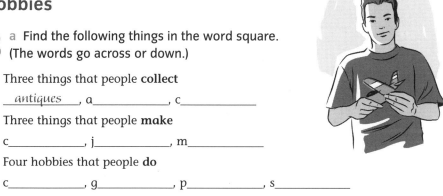

1 Three things that people **collect**

_antiques_ , a_____ , c_____

2 Three things that people **make**

c_____ , j_____ , m_____

3 Four hobbies that people **do**

c_____ , g_____ , p_____ , s_____

4 Four hobbies with **go**

d_____ , f_____ , s_____ , s_____

| B | M | C | R | O | S | S | W | O | R | D | S |
|---|---|---|---|---|---|---|---|---|---|---|---|
| A | N | T | I | Q | U | E | S | P | A | A | L |
| U | S | P | G | A | R | D | E | N | I | N | G |
| T | S | W | M | N | F | Q | C | V | J | C | G |
| O | F | I | S | H | I | N | G | B | T | I | P |
| G | R | A | C | M | N | K | C | O | I | N | S |
| R | Z | G | L | R | G | W | E | T | K | G | A |
| A | H | M | O | D | E | L | S | E | M | Q | I |
| P | H | O | T | O | G | R | A | P | H | Y | L |
| H | B | C | H | X | U | U | D | L | M | A | I |
| S | D | J | E | W | E | L | L | E | R | Y | N |
| A | W | P | S | P | O | R | T | T | L | S | G |

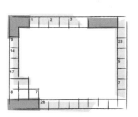

b Complete the sentences with the correct form of *collect*, *make*, *do* or *go*.

1 My brother ____goes____ fishing every weekend, but he never catches anything!

2 Don't disturb your mother – she's _____ a crossword.

3 Christina _____ all her own clothes, and she always looks fantastic.

4 Do you want to _____ dancing tonight? There's a salsa evening at the community centre.

5 My uncle says he _____ antiques because it's a good way of investing money.

6 My friend Will's _____ a beautiful model of an old sailing boat at the moment.

7 Kim's really fit and healthy because she _____ a lot of sport every week.

8 I've decided to _____ famous chefs' autographs – I've got two, so far!

# Vocabulary
## People around you

9 Unjumble the letters to find ten people from the box on page 10 of the Students' Book.

| | | |
|---|---|---|
| 1 | cenie | n _iece_____ |
| 2 | reptan | p_____ |
| 3 | tvealrie | r _____ |
| 4 | tregrasn | s _____ |
| 5 | inoscu | c_____ |
| 6 | qacanenuciat | a_____ |
| 7 | saslecmat | c_____ |
| 8 | goulelace | c_____ |
| 9 | pomstether | s _____ |
| 10 | bunigoher | n_____ |

## Pronunciation
## The letter 's'

LOOK!

The letter 's' can be pronounced /s/, /z/ or /ɪz/ in:
- plural forms of nouns, e.g.
  flatmate**s**, neighbour**s**,
       /s/         /z/
  marriage**s**
    /ɪz/
- Present simple, third person singular, e.g.
  she smoke**s**, he learn**s**,
      /s/        /z/
  it increase**s**
      /ɪz/

**10** **T1.3** Listen to the nouns and verbs in the box (or say them aloud) and complete the table below.

| wants | nieces | spells |
|---|---|---|
| practises | parents | hopes |
| uses | classmates | pronounces |
| colleagues | works | spends |
| entertains | relatives | |
| acquaintances | | |

| /s/ | /z/ | /ɪz/ |
|---|---|---|
| wants | | |
| | | |
| | | |
| | | |
| | | |

## Listen and read
## Ordinary heroes

**11** **a** **T1.4** A TV station is doing some research for a programme about ordinary people who are considered 'heroes' by people around them. Listen to and/or read the e-mails and answer the questions.

Whose hero is …

1 a stranger? _____

2 a relative? _____

3 a colleague? _____

**1**

My 'hero' at the moment is Ricky; we work together. I was thinking of leaving the place where I work because of our horrible new boss. He's always in a bad mood and he never has a good word to say to anyone. He also picks on young female members of staff: there's a girl called Kimberley who's terrified of him. Or a least she was. When Ricky joined us, everything changed. First he covered for me when I was late back from lunch by telling the boss that I was downstairs in the photocopying room. Then a couple of days later the boss was standing at Kimberley's desk, shouting at her, telling her she was lazy and would have to stay late to finish her work … anyway, Ricky marched straight up to him and told him he was a pathetic coward for talking to his staff like that. Well, the boss was stunned to silence – he just walked off without saying another word and he's left us alone since then.
**Charlotte, Bristol**

**2**

I'm writing to tell you about my niece, Mary. She's only seven and she's in hospital at the moment. She was in a bad car accident two weeks ago and she broke both her legs. She's had one operation and now she's waiting for another, then she'll have to be in a wheelchair for quite a while. Anyway, I am constantly amazed by this little girl's courage: she never cries when she has an injection, and very rarely complains about the considerable pain that she must be in. When I go in to visit her she always has a smile for me, and last time I went she was comforting another girl who was upset because her parents couldn't come and visit her. I've also noticed that she shares all the chocolates and toys that people have given her with the other children in her ward. I don't know how many adults would be as generous as that!
**Dan, Newcastle**

**3**

I'm hoping that by writing to you, I might be able to get in touch with my 'hero' again. I don't know him – I don't even know his name – but what he did was unbelievably kind and honest. I went shopping at my local supermarket last Friday, and I met an old friend at the checkout desk. We chatted for a while, then I loaded up the car and came home. It was only then that I realised I'd lost my purse: I thought maybe I'd dropped it in the car park. I started to panic when I also remembered that I had quite a lot of money in it. Then someone knocked at the door and it was a complete stranger, holding out my purse! He said he was in the queue behind me at the supermarket checkout and that's where he found my purse. He got my address from my driving licence. I was so grateful, but I didn't know what to say. Anyway, he just walked off, and I haven't been able to thank him properly.
**Annette, Leeds**

**b** Listen and/or read again and answer the questions.

Who ...
1   is very brave? _____
2   nearly left her job? _____
3   nearly lost a lot of money? _____
4   was terrified of her boss? _____
5   is in a lot of pain? _____
6   told his boss what he thought of him? _____
7   is more generous than many adults? _____
8   wants to contact his/her hero? _____

## Present simple

**12** **a** Read the three extracts. Which is from ...

1   ☐   a detective story?
2   ☐   an encyclopaedia?
3   ☐   an e-mail to a pen friend?

**b** Complete the extracts with the Present simple form of the verbs in the box under each extract.

**A**

|  Message  |
| --- |
| ⏎Reply  ⏎Reply All  ➦Forward  🖨 📠 ✖  ⇧ ⇩  ✉Follow Up  🅰 ▾ |

We (a) ___live___ in Lisbon. My parents (b) _____ a furniture shop, and I (c) _____ them in the shop at weekends. Please write back and tell me about you and your family. What (d) _____ you _____ like? (Can you send a photo?) What (e) _____ your parents _____ ? And what about the weather in England? (f) _____ it really _____ all the time?

| do   help   ~~live~~   look   own   rain |
| --- |

**B**

'So who (a) _____ the gun _____ to, Smith?'
'Well, Inspector, we (b) _____ that only three people in the village (c) _____ a gun, but we (d) _____ which of them had a motive for killing the Professor. Let's go back to the scene of the crime – I (e) _____ to try an experiment. (f) _____ you _____ in telepathy, Inspector Turner?'

| believe   belong   not know   own   think   want |
| --- |

**C**

The koala is an Australian mammal. It
(a) _____ thick fur and round ears but it
(b) _____ a tail, like a teddy bear. Koalas
(c) _____ most of the day sleeping. They
(d) _____ water, but they (e) _____
liquids from eating eucalyptus leaves. The word
*koala* (f) _____ from the Aborigine word
meaning 'no drink'.

| come   get   not drink   have   not have   spend |
| --- |

## Spelling
## The *-ing* form

> LOOK!
>
> To make the *-ing* form, we usually add *-ing* to the baseform of the verb: *sleeping, reading, studying*.
>
> There are three exceptions:
> • One-syllable verbs with consonant + vowel + consonant (e.g. *put*): double the final consonant: *putting*. (We do not double *x, y* or *w*: *boxing, buying, knowing*.)
> • Verbs which end in *-e*: lose the *-e*: *make – making*.
> • Two-syllable verbs which are stressed on the second syllable (e.g. *forget, begin*): double the final consonant: *forgetting, beginning*. (An exception to this is *travelling*.)

**13** Write the *-ing* form of the verbs.

a   read       ___reading___
b   pay        _____
c   write      _____
d   see        _____
e   begin      _____
f   fax        _____
g   hope       _____
h   plan       _____
i   jog        _____
j   open       _____
k   copy       _____
l   answer     _____
m   hurry      _____
n   grow       _____
o   drive      _____

**11**

## Present continuous

14 Complete the sentences with the Present continuous form of the verbs in the boxes.

| breath | clean | die | eat | get (x2) | have |
|---|---|---|---|---|---|
| not do | not get | not set | spend | stay | |
| suffer | talk | use | visit | watch | |

'This is Sandra Wise with the news headlines: the President (a) _____is visiting_____ the UK this week: he and his wife (b) _____ at London's famous Savoy Hotel. Today he (c) _____ a meeting with the British Prime Minister, and later in the week ...'

'... later on Ten News tonight: why we as a nation (d) _____ fat: a nutrition expert says that our children (e) _____ too much junk food and (f) _____ enough exercise, and as parents we (g) _____ a good example: we (h) _____ more time than ever in the car or in front of the TV ...'

'... and finally, (i) _____ your health _____ because of indoor pollution? (j) _____ you _____ in dangerous chemicals while you sit at home watching this programme? According to a report by the Clean Air Society, this is a serious problem for millions of people. The president of the society even claims that people (k) _____ because of the air they breathe in their own homes.'

KRIS: Hi, Robin, it's Kris. (l) _____ you _____ the news on TV?

ROBIN: No, actually I (m) _____ the kitchen! I (n) _____ ready for Sammy's party tomorrow.

KRIS: (o) _____ you _____ a cleaner with chemicals in it?

ROBIN: Well, yes, I suppose. Kris, what (p) _____ you _____ about?

KRIS: Oh, it's just that there was an item about indoor pollution, and ...

## Present simple or continuous

15 Mike, a salesman, is talking to his doctor about his stress problems. Complete the conversation with the Present simple or continuous of the verbs in brackets.

DOCTOR: How can I help you, Mr Daniels?

MIKE: Well, I started having bad headaches a couple of weeks ago and they (a) _'re getting_____ (get) worse. I can't sleep properly, I'm tired all the time, and the worst thing is my hair (b) _____ (go) grey and I'm only 31!

DOCTOR: I see. Let me ask you some questions. (c) _____ (you smoke)?

MIKE: No, I gave up a month ago.

DOCTOR: Right. I see you're a salesman. How many hours a week (d) _____ (you work)?

MIKE: Well, I normally (e) _____ (do) eight hours a day, but at the moment I (f) _____ (work) at least ten hours and some Saturdays.

DOCTOR: That is a lot. How (g) _____ (you relax)?

MIKE: Well, I usually (h) _____ (sit) in front of the TV with a pizza and a few beers.

DOCTOR: Hmm. (i) _____ (you do) any exercise at the moment?

MIKE: Not really, but I'm losing a lot of weight and I (j) _____ (not know) why.

DOCTOR: I think you (k) _____ (suffer) from stress. I (l) _____ (want) you to eat a more varied diet and to do some exercise. Come back and see me in four weeks and I'll check you again.

## Wordspot
### *have* and *have got*

**16** Complete the sentences with a phrase from the box and the correct form of *have*.

| | | | |
|---|---|---|---|
| a break | a walk | blue eyes | a bad back |
| a~~ cold drink~~ | a shower | breakfast | a sense of humour |

a   It's so hot! Let's stop in this café and _have a cold drink_ .

b   All the people in my family _____ and black hair.

c   Can we stop and _____ soon? I'm getting tired.

d   You need to _____ in this job – things are always going wrong!

e   Marc's just _____ – he'll be down in a few minutes.

f   Why is it that you always _____ when I need you to help with the housework?

g   I think I'll _____ before dinner – I need some fresh air.

h   I like to _____ in a café on Sunday mornings, and read all the papers.

## Improve your writing
### Responding to news

**17** **a** Read Laura's reply to Charlotte's e-mail on page 14 of the Students' Book. What does she write about first: her own news or her response to Charlotte's news?

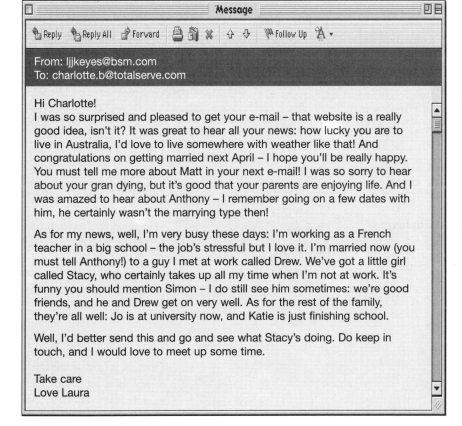

```
                    Message
Reply   Reply All   Forward         Follow Up

From: ljjkeyes@bsm.com
To: charlotte.b@totalserve.com

Hi Charlotte!
I was so surprised and pleased to get your e-mail – that website is a really
good idea, isn't it? It was great to hear all your news: how lucky you are to
live in Australia, I'd love to live somewhere with weather like that! And
congratulations on getting married next April – I hope you'll be really happy.
You must tell me more about Matt in your next e-mail! I was so sorry to hear
about your gran dying, but it's good that your parents are enjoying life. And I
was amazed to hear about Anthony – I remember going on a few dates with
him, he certainly wasn't the marrying type then!

As for my news, well, I'm very busy these days: I'm working as a French
teacher in a big school – the job's stressful but I love it. I'm married now (you
must tell Anthony!) to a guy I met at work called Drew. We've got a little girl
called Stacy, who certainly takes up all my time when I'm not at work. It's
funny you should mention Simon – I do still see him sometimes: we're good
friends, and he and Drew get on very well. As for the rest of the family,
they're all well: Jo is at university now, and Katie is just finishing school.

Well, I'd better send this and go and see what Stacy's doing. Do keep in
touch, and I would love to meet up some time.

Take care
Love Laura
```

**b** Write the phrases from the e-mail that Laura uses to respond to the following.

1   getting Charlotte's e-mail
_I was so surprised and pleased_
_to get your e-mail._

2   hearing Charlotte's news
_____
_____ .

3   the news that Charlotte lives in Australia
_____
_____ .

4   the news about Charlotte's wedding
_____
_____ .

5   the news about Charlotte's gran's death
_____
_____ .

6   the news about Anthony
_____
_____ .

7   Charlotte's question about Simon
_____
_____ .

**c** Write a phrase to respond to the following things.

1   Your friend sent you some photos of her new baby.
_____
_____ .

2   Your friend's new house has a swimming pool.
_____
_____ .

3   Your friend passed his driving test.
_____
_____ .

4   Your friend's brother lost his job and you were shocked.
_____
_____ .

# MODULE 2

## Past simple

**1** Complete the dialogues with the Past simple form of the verbs in the box.

| | | | | |
|---|---|---|---|---|
| cook | forget | get (x2) | go | happen |
| hear | introduce | rain | ring | stay |
| ~~not see~~ | not tell | not want | | |

A: Oh sorry, I (a) ___didn't see___ you there.

(b) _____ you _____ the bell?

B: No, I (c) _____ to disturb you.

A: (d) _____ you _____ out last night?

B: No, actually we (e) _____ in and Gary (f) _____ a fantastic meal.

A: (g) _____ you _____ about Abby and Rob's disastrous holiday?

B: No, what (h) _____ ?

A: Well, the weather was terrible – it (i) _____ every day, and they both (j) _____ food poisoning from the hotel food!

A: Why (k) _____ you _____ me about Marc's engagement? I (l) _____ quite a shock when he (m) _____ me to his fiancée.

B: Oh, I'm so sorry. I (n) _____ to tell you. She's nice, isn't she?

## Spelling
### Past simple forms

**2** **a** Look again at the rules for spelling the *-ing* form on page 11 of the Workbook. The rules are the same for spelling the Past simple form (ending in *-ed* not *-ing*). Complete the table.

| | | *-ing* form | Past simple |
|---|---|---|---|
| 1 | stop | *stopping* | *stopped* |
| 2 | train | _____ | _____ |
| 3 | plan | _____ | _____ |
| 4 | look | _____ | _____ |
| 5 | fax | _____ | _____ |
| 6 | phone | _____ | _____ |
| 7 | offer | _____ | _____ |
| 8 | travel | _____ | _____ |
| 9 | allow | _____ | _____ |
| 10 | change | _____ | _____ |

> **LOOK!**
>
> Verbs ending in consonant + *y*, change *y* to *i* and add *-ed*: *cry – cried*.
>
> Verbs ending in a vowel + *y*, don't change the *y*: *pray – prayed*.
>
> Note: There are two exceptions: *say – said*, *pay – paid*.

**b** Write the past form of these verbs.

| | | |
|---|---|---|
| 1 | try | ___tried___ |
| 2 | enjoy | _____ |
| 3 | hurry | _____ |
| 4 | play | _____ |
| 5 | pay | _____ |
| 6 | employ | _____ |
| 7 | stay | _____ |
| 8 | dry | _____ |
| 9 | apply | _____ |
| 10 | say | _____ |

## Pronunciation
### Syllable stress in Past simple forms

**3** **a** How many syllables do these *-ed* forms have?
Mark the stressed syllables ● and the unstressed syllables ○.

1  [2]  háppèned
2  [1]  stópped
3  [ ]  travelled
4  [ ]  looked
5  [ ]  reminded
6  [ ]  visited
7  [ ]  phoned
8  [ ]  changed
9  [ ]  practised
10 [ ]  opened
11 [ ]  improved
12 [ ]  received
13 [ ]  repeated
14 [ ]  answered

**b** 〖T2.1〗 Listen to the verbs in phrases and repeat them.

## Past continuous

**4** Complete the sentences with the Present continuous form of the verbs in brackets.

a  I'm sorry I'm late, I ___*was waiting*___ (wait) for the babysitter.

b  Who _____ (you talk) to on the phone just now?

c  Sorry, I _____ (not concentrate) – can you explain that again, please?

d  A: I saw Lee in the jewellery store on Saturday.
   B: Oh! What _____ (he do)?
   A: Well, he _____ (buy) a diamond ring!

e  A: How do you work this thing again?
   B: No idea! I _____ (not listen) when he explained it to us.

f  A: Why wasn't Mia at work yesterday?
   B: I think she _____ (move) house.

g  I saw Renée with her new boyfriend yesterday: They _____ (have) an argument.

h  Sorry, _____ (we make) a lot of noise?
   We _____ (put) up some shelves.

## Past simple or continuous

**5** Choose a phrase from each box to make a complete answer for the questions below.

| |
|---|
| I was peeling ~~some~~ ~~onions~~ and |
| She was travelling home from work and she |
| We were sunbathing at the weekend and we |
| They were staying in Florida when |
| He was walking in the rain and he |
| He was playing football and he |

| |
|---|
| got very wet. |
| stayed out too long. |
| ~~the knife slipped.~~ |
| left it on the bus. |
| fell over. |
| there was a terrible storm. |

a  How did you cut your finger?
   *I was peeling some onions and the knife slipped.*

b  How did Tony hurt his knee?
   _____
   _____

c  How did you all get so sunburnt?
   _____
   _____

d  How did Martin catch a cold?
   _____
   _____

e  How did a tree fall on the Simpson's car?
   _____
   _____

f  How did Sarah lose her bag?
   _____
   _____

**6** Complete the dialogues with the best form of the verbs in brackets.

A: I phoned you last night at 8.00 but you didn't answer. What (a) _were you doing_ (you do)?

B: I (b) _____ (work) on my computer and I (c) _____ (not hear) the phone ring.

A: Good Morning. ICI. May I help you?

B: Hello, yes. I (d) _____ (talk) to the Financial Director a minute ago and the line (e) _____ (go) dead.

A: Oh, I'm sorry, Madam. I'll reconnect you.

A: When did you meet your husband?

B: When I (f) _____ (be) in Canada four years ago.

A: Were you on holiday?

B: No, I (g) _____ (train) to be a ski instructor, but I (h) _____ (break) my leg. I (i) _____ (spend) eight weeks in hospital and he was my doctor!

**7** Use the prompts to write two conversations about accidents.

A A: Penny told me you / have / accident yesterday. What / happen?
(1) _Penny told me you had an accident_
_yesterday. What happened?_

B: We / drive / home and another car / stop / suddenly and we / crash / into the back of it.
(2) _____
_____

A: Be / the other car all right?
(3) _____

B: Yes, luckily we / not go / very fast.
(4) _____
_____

B A: What / you / do to your hand?
(1) _____

B: I / burn / it.
(2) _____

A: Oh no, how?

B: I / iron/ a shirt, and the phone / ring, and I / put / the iron down on my hand by mistake!
(3) _____
_____

# Improve your writing
## Using *when*, *while*, *during* and *for* in stories

> **LOOK!**
>
> When we talk about actions or situations that take place at the same time, we can use *when* or *while*.
> • *Maggie hurt her leg when/while she was jogging.*
> • *I was talking to Penny when/while you were playing tennis.*
>
> If we are talking about a single event at a particular time, we can only use *when*.
> • *Jane was sixteen when she first met David.*
>
> Look at these examples using *during* and *for*:
> • *I'm staying with my cousin **during** the holidays.* (= part of the holidays)
> • *I'm staying with my cousin **for** the holidays.* (= the whole of the holidays)
>
> Note: We use *during/for* with nouns.

**8** **a** Below is part of a letter Jenny wrote to her brother, describing her terrible week. Complete the letter with *when, while, during* or *for*.

... and then on Thursday, I took a new client out to lunch at that French restaurant in the centre of town. What a disaster! Everything was fine at first – we got a nice table, but (1) _when_ they started playing music, we found we were next to the speakers. We changed tables and ordered our meal. We waited (2) _____ half an hour before the waiter brought the wine, and then (3) _____ he was pouring it he spilt it all over my client's suit.

She said, 'Don't worry', but I could see she was very angry, so (4) _____ we were having the first course, the atmosphere was quite tense. Then (5) _____ we were waiting for the main course, the couple on the next table started having a loud argument!

The worst thing was (6) _____ the bill came, I realised I'd left my credit cared at home. I felt really embarrassed and in the end she had to pay. And that wasn't all – I said goodbye to her and went to the car park and found that someone had stolen my car radio (7) _____ the meal.

**b** Use the pictures and prompts to write the story. Use the Past simple and continuous and *when*, *while*, *during* or *for*. Also remember to use *and* and *so* to join parts of a sentence.

Alan is talking about his weekend. On Saturday he went to his friend Kyra's party. Another friend, Guy, offered to take him to the party in his car.

Pictures 1 and 2: I / get dressed / Guy / phone – say / he / be / ill – I / decide / go by train

(1) *I was getting dressed when Guy phoned and said he was ill, so I decided to go by train.*

Picture 3: Unfortunately / I / talk to Guy on phone / cat / walk over my shirt – I / have to / iron another one

(2) _____

Picture 4: I / walk / station start / snowing – I / get / cold

(3) _____

Picture 5: I / have to / wait / half an hour on the platform – train / finally arrive / I / be / frozen

(4) _____

Picture 6: I / fall asleep / journey – miss / station

(5) _____

Picture 7: I / get off / next station – decide / walk / Kyra's house – I / walk / half an hour / I / realise / I / be / lost

(6) _____

Picture 8: I / not have / my mobile – I / look for / phone box / call / taxi

(7) _____

Picture 9: I / arrive / Kyra's house / it / be / nearly midnight – people / go / home

(8) _____

**c** 🔊 **T2.2** Listen to the recording and compare the story with your version.

## Listen and read
### I used to believe

9 a **T2.3** Listen to and/or read these extracts from a website where people write in about their childhood beliefs. Which stories are shown in the pictures below?

**A**  ☐

**B**  ☐

**C**  ☐

**D**  ☐

b **Match the stories to the topics below.**

| 3 | time |
|---|------|
| ☐ | language |
| ☐ | animals |
| ☐ | transport |
| ☐ | countries |
| ☐ | politics |
| ☐ | drink |
| ☐ | food |
| ☐ | teachers |
| ☐ | kitchen appliances |

# I used to believe

1  'I used to believe that countries really had their names written across them and that when you reached a border there would be red dotted lines on the ground.'

2  'I used to think that the trails that aeroplanes leave across the sky are created by the pilots leaning out of the windows holding a piece of chalk, so they know where they've been. That's what I was told, anyway.'

3  'I used to have problems when I was trying to learn how to read a real clock. My theory was that if an hour is longer than a minute, then the long hand was the hour and the short hand was for minutes. I was always late coming home … or really early.'

4  'I remember I used to be very scared of swallowing seeds when I was small. Once when I swallowed a lemon pip, I refused to open my mouth in the morning because I thought that the branches of the lemon tree that had grown in the night would come out.'

5  'When I was about six or seven years old I used to believe that a little penguin lived in my refrigerator and his job was to turn the interior light on and off. I used to sit and open the fridge repeatedly, trying to catch him doing it.'

6  'For some reason, I used to think that there was a big red button in the middle of the President's desk, and if he pressed it the whole world would explode. I also thought that it wasn't very well guarded, and I always worried that he would accidentally lean on it.'

7  'One time when I was about to pour a drink from a bottle of diet coke, my sister said "You know, diet coke turns you into a skeleton if you're not fat." I was terrified. Unfortunately for me, her lie worked and I didn't drink any diet drinks until I was in my teens.'

8  'When I was a child, I couldn't understand how a radio made in Japan could play songs in Spanish and English. If they are made in Japan, they should just be able to play Japanese songs.'

9  'During my first few years at school I kept hearing that "teachers have eyes in the back of their heads" so I thought that when someone became a teacher, they had to have an operation to get an extra set of eyes! I also wondered why a lot of lady teachers had long hair. What's the point of having eyes in the back of your head if you keep covering them up?'

10 'I used to believe (and still do actually!) that animals could watch TV and understand what they were seeing. I had a rabbit that just sat near the screen, staring at it while the show was on, but would look away or do something else when the ads came on. Now my two dogs act in the same way – they sit with me and watch TV, but then start to yawn and stretch during the ads – except dog food commercials, of course!

## used to

**10** **a** Look at the pictures and notes about Virginia's life ten years ago and now. Write eight sentences about how her life has changed, using *used to* and *didn't use to*.

1  She used to live in England.

2  _____

3  _____

4  _____

5  _____

6  _____

7  _____

8  _____

**b** Now write eight sentences using *still* and *not ... any more / any longer*.

1  *She still wears fashionable clothes.*

2  *She doesn't live in England any more.*

3  _____

4  _____

5  _____

6  _____

7  _____

8  _____

travel / all over the world

have / long hair

sing / in a band

keep / fit

earn / a lot of money

live / in England

wear / fashionable clothes

ride / a motorbike

live / in Italy

be / married to a famous footballer

have / long hair

have / two children

earn / a lot of money

wear / fashionable clothes

design / sports clothes

keep / fit

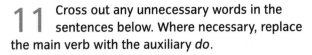

## 11 Cross out any unnecessary words in the sentences below. Where necessary, replace the main verb with the auxiliary *do*.

a   I used to have long hair but I don't ~~have long hair~~ any more.

b   My friends and I didn't use to go to the gym every week, but now we go to the gym every week.

c   My boyfriend used to be a terrible cook, but he isn't a terrible cook any more.

d   There used to be a lot of traffic in my city, and there still is a lot of traffic.

e   I didn't use to know how to send text messages, but now I know how to send text messages.

f   My younger brother used to be shorter than me, but now he isn't shorter than me.

g   I didn't use to like spiders and I still don't like spiders!

h   My family didn't use to go overseas for our holidays, but now we go overseas for our holidays.

i   I used to be very shy but I'm not shy any longer.

j   My sister didn't use to send a lot of e-mails, but now she sends a lot of e-mails.

## Vocabulary booster
## School/University subjects

## 12 a Which subjects are the people below talking about? Write the name of the subject next to the appropriate comment.

| | |
|---|---|
| art | biology |
| chemistry | drama |
| economics | geography |
| history | information technology (IT) |
| languages | literature |
| mathematics (maths) | media studies |
| music | physical education (PE) |
| psychology | religious studies |

1   'I could never remember the names of all the authors.'  _literature_

2   'I enjoyed this because I was interested in animals and plants.'  _____

3   'My worst subject – I always got all my sums wrong.'  _____

4   'I loved doing experiments in the lab.'  _____

5   'I found them difficult – I couldn't understand the grammar.'  _____

6   'There were a lot of dates to learn, but the teacher really brought it to life for us.'  _____

7   'I found it interesting to see how biased the different newspapers are.'  _____

8   'I liked finding places in the atlas, but I was no good at remembering the names of the capital cities.'  _____

9   'One of my favourite subjects – I loved dressing up and learning lines.'  _____

10   'I hated it – I've never been good at team games!'  _____

11   'I wasn't very good at it but I found painting really relaxing and liked experimenting with different colours.'  _____

12   'It was a difficult subject, but very interesting to find out how the mind works.'  _____

13   'This was my best subject. I played the piano and sang in the school choir.'  _____

14   'I found it boring and I still do: just ask my bank manager!'  _____

15   'I think it's important to learn about different people's beliefs.'  _____

16   'A very useful subject to study at school, especially when most people will use computers at some point in their lives.'  _____

b   **T2.4**   Listen and check. Then listen and mark the stressed syllable.

•
literature

c   Which subject at school …

1   is/was your favourite? Why?

_____

_____

2   do/did you find difficult? Why?

_____

_____

3   do/did you find interesting? Why?

_____

_____

4   do/did you hate? Why?

_____

_____

## Vocabulary
### Verb + noun combinations

13 Complete the sentences with the correct form of the verbs in the box. The verb + noun combinations are from pages 20 and 21 of the Students' Book.

> ask    do    improve    invent    lose    make (x2)
> organise    reduce    take (x2)

a   I didn't ___make___ many notes during the lesson.

b   Doing exercise is a good way to _____ stress.

c   I hope I don't _____ my memory as quickly as you did, grandad!

d   I've tried to get Tilly to _____ an interest in sport, but she says it's boring.

e   Why don't you try to _____ your ideas before you start writing the essay – then it'll be easier.

f   Come on Ali, you're not _____ an effort – I'm sure you know the answer.

g   Max decided to _____ his memory by repeating things lots of times and by _____ himself lots of questions.

h   After the lesson, Narinder _____ a funny story to help him remember the new English words.

i   I'm surprised my dad hasn't got a better memory: he loves _____ puzzles.

j   Jake is _____ more responsibility for his learning now, and his progress is excellent.

## Vocabulary
### Remembering and forgetting

14 a Complete the questions with remember, remind, forget, recognise, learn or lose.

1   When you argue with a friend, do you ___forget___ about it quickly and stay friends?

2   Do you find it easy to _____ people's names?

3   How long did it take you to _____ how to use a computer?

4   When did you last _____ someone's birthday?

5   Is it easy to _____ your handwriting?

6   Do you _____ people of anyone in your family?

7   Can you _____ your first day at school?

8   Have you ever had to _____ a poem by heart?

9   How often do you _____ your keys?

10   What sort of things do people have to _____ you to do?

b   T2.5 Listen and check. Then answer the questions about yourself.

## Real life and pronunciation
### Short questions to show interest

15 a Complete the questions with the correct auxiliary verb.

1   A: My cousin lives next door to Brad Pitt.
    B: ___Does___ he? Wow!

2   A: My grandfather's learning Italian.
    B: _____ he?

3   A: We don't have to go to school this week.
    B: _____ we? Great!

4   A: My dad wasn't in a very good mood last night.
    B: _____ he? I wonder why?

5   A: My parents want to meet you.
    B: _____ they? Oh!

6   A: Our neighbours have got a cow in their garden.
    B: _____ they? How strange!

7   A: I didn't really understand that lesson.
    B: _____ you? It was easy!

8   A: My best friend and her family are moving to Canada.
    B: _____ they? When?

9   A: We lost all our luggage at the airport.
    B: Oh no! _____ you?

10   A: My little sister was only two when she learnt how to swim.
    B: _____ she?

b   T2.6 Listen and repeat the questions. Notice that the stress is always on the auxiliary verb, not on the pronoun, and intonation is rising.

•          •           •
was he?   did you?   are they?

## Comparatives and superlatives

### 1 Correct the mistakes.

a  Nowadays flying is sometimes ~~more cheap~~ than going by train. *cheaper*

b  The easyest way to book your holiday is on the Internet.

c  I'd like to hire a car – I know it's more expensive the train or bus, but it's more convenient.

d  The worse thing about camping is all the insects that you find in your tent!

e  Phuket was our more popular destination last year, so you need to book early.

f  We went to London last August, and it was hoter than I expected.

g  I think we should go to Indonesia in March – that's when you get best deals.

h  Most places are busy during the school holidays than at other times of the year.

i  We always go to the same place – I want to go somewhere more far away this year.

j  It says in the brochure that New Zealand has the cleanest beaches of the world.

### 2 a Sean wants to celebrate his birthday at a nightclub. He's got information from three clubs in the city. Complete the conversation with the comparative or superlative form of the adjectives in the box.

| big | central | ~~cheap~~ | crowded | expensive | far | friendly | good |
| quiet | successful | | | | | | |

SEAN:  I think *All Nite Long* looks good: my friends haven't got much money and it's (1) ___the cheapest___ of the three places. It's also (2) _____ ; they can take 250 people, and it's (3) _____ so people could get there easily.

MEERA:  But Paradiso has got (4) _____ music than All Nite Long – they haven't got real bands there.

JUSTIN:  Actually, I think you should go to Liam's Place: I know it's (5) _____ away than the other two, but because it's small, it's got a (6) _____ atmosphere: the big clubs are too impersonal. Also, it's much (7) _____ if people want to talk.

MEERA:  Well, Paradiso isn't noisy at all. I know it's (8) _____ nightclub in town, but for €10 you can get live music and a great atmosphere.

JUSTIN :  But you know it's much (9) _____ than Liam's Place: you often can't get a table.

MEERA:  Well, that's because it's (10) _____ club in the north-west at the moment – everyone wants to go there.

SEAN:  Hold on! It's my birthday, remember, and I want …

LIAM'S PLACE

*Smokey Joe's Jazz Band*

€8.50 entrance
*Maximum 75 people*

Dress: jacket and tie

Only 15 minutes from the city train station

LIAM'S PLACE

**All Nite Long**

*DJ Max plays your favourite rock & pop*

€7 entrance
Maximum 250 people

*IN THE CITY CENTRE*

**Paradiso**
*Dance to 'Los Gitanos'*

€10 entrance

Maximum 150 people
Dress: no jeans please

Only 10 minutes from the centre

b  **T3.1**  Listen to some phrases from the conversation and repeat them.

**3** Look at the information from a review of digital cameras and circle the correct alternative in each sentence.

|  | F104 | Coolshot | Quikpix |
|---|---|---|---|
| size | 8cm x 6cm x 2cm | 10cm x 7cm x 2cm | 12cm x 9cm x 2cm |
| weight | 85g | 90g | 95g |
| appearance | 9/10 | 3/10 | 7/10 |
| reliability | 3/10 | 10/10 | 9/10 |
| picture quality | 5/10 | 9/10 | 10/10 |
| easy to use | 8/10 | 10/10 | 10/10 |
| value for money | 2/10 | 5/10 | 10/10 |
| popularity rating | ★ | ★ ★ | ★ ★ ★ |

a   The Coolshot is *much heavier /* *slightly heavier* than the F104.

b   The Coolshot is *the second most popular / the most popular* in the range.

c   The F104 is *far better looking / slightly better looking* than the Coolshot.

d   The F104 is *the most reliable / the least reliable* of the three.

e   The Quikpix is *the easiest / one of the easiest* digital cameras to use.

f   The Coolshot is *a little bit lighter / a lot lighter* than the Quikpix.

g   The Quikpix is *slightly bigger / a lot bigger* than the F104.

h   The Quikpix has got *much better / slightly better* picture quality than the F104.

i   The Coolshot is *a lot more reliable / a little more reliable* than the Quikpix.

j   The Quikpix is *the second best / by far the best* value for money on the market.

# Vocabulary booster
## Geographical features

**4 a** Answer the questions.

1   a river, a canal, a stream
Which is the narrowest? _____
Which is man-made? _____

2   a canyon, a valley, a cliff
Which can you see in the picture?

Which is deeper: a canyon or a valley?
_____

3   a sea, an ocean
Which is bigger? _____
Which can be inland? _____

4   a mountain, a hill, a volcano
Which has got a hole in the top? _____
Which is smaller: a mountain or a hill? _____

5   a waterfall, a spring
Which can you see in the picture? _____

Which way does the water come from a spring: up or down? _____

6   a field, a meadow, a desert
Which has got flowers and grass in it, but not for cows and sheep to eat? _____
Which is made of sand? _____

7   an island, a reef
Which is under the sea? _____

8   a beach, a coast
Which can you see in the picture?

9   a harbour, a bay
Which is an area of deep water where ships are safe? _____

10   a lake, a lagoon
Which has got sea water in it? _____

**b** T3.2 Listen and practise the pronunciation of the words.

## Different phrases for comparing

**5** Complete the sentences comparing the UK and Australia with the words in the box.

| as (x2) | completely | different | ~~from~~ | less |
| more | similar | slightly | the | to |

---

**UK and Australia:**
*the same or different?*

a The climate in Australia is different __from__ the climate in the UK.

b Australian coins look similar _____ British coins.

c A lot of wild animals in Australia are _____ different from the wild animals that you find in England.

d Supermarkets in Australia are exactly the same _____ supermarkets in the UK.

e The cost of living in Sydney is very _____ to the cost of living in London.

f Houses in the British countryside look very _____ from houses in the Australian countryside.

g Australian TV programmes are _____ or _____ the same as British TV programmes.

h Australian road signs are _____ different from road signs in the UK.

i Daily life in Australia is about _____ same _____ daily life in the UK.

---

**6** Look at the following sentences and make one complete sentence, using the word in bold.

a A meal in the Four Seasons restaurant costs €15. A meal in the Pizza Parlour costs €11. **less**
A meal in the Pizza Parlour costs *less than a meal in the Four Seasons restaurant.*

b The Manor Hotel is €50 a night. The Park Hotel is €75. **expensive**
The Manor Hotel isn't _____
_____ .

c Savewell supermarket has 2,000 customers a day. Pricerite supermarket has 1,500. **more**
Savewell supermarket _____
_____ .

d There are three trains an hour in the afternoon. There are five trains an hour in the morning. **fewer**
There are _____
_____ .

e The furniture in my sister's flat is more or less the same as Tim's. **similar**
The furniture in my sister's flat _____
_____ .

f The Guggenheim Museum in Bilbao is made mostly of metal. The Guggenheim Museum in New York looks like a concrete multi-storey car park. **different**
The Guggenheim Museum in New York _____
_____ .

g Phil's flat has four rooms and a balcony. My flat's opposite his, and it's got four rooms and a balcony, too. **same**
My flat's _____
_____ .

## Pronunciation
### /ð/ and /θ/

**7** a **T3.3** Listen to the words in the box (or say them aloud) and complete the table.

| the | north | than | this | theatre | there | both |
| fourth | further | south | through | that | thing |
| third | other | weather |

| /ð/ | /θ/ |
| --- | --- |
| *the* | *north* |
|  |  |
|  |  |
|  |  |
|  |  |
|  |  |

b **T3.4** Listen and repeat the sentences.

1 The theatre's just over there.
2 That was my fourth visit to the city.
3 It's further south than that.
4 This is the third time we've been here.
5 We both came here the other day.
6 The best thing about this country is the weather.

## Vocabulary
### Describing towns and cities

**8** Use the clues to complete the grid. All the words can be found in Vocabulary and writing on page 31 of the Students' Book.

a quiet and calm
b important in history
c connected with industry
d makes you think about love or adventure
e full of people, buildings, etc.
f impressive and dramatic to look at

g not modern
h dangerously dirty (to describe air and water)
i the opposite of *quiet*
j the opposite of *dull* and *uninteresting*
k liked by lots of people
l a beach without stones

|   |   |   |   |   |   |   |   |
|---|---|---|---|---|---|---|---|
| a P | E | A | C | E | F | U | L |
|  |  | O |  |  |  |  |  |
|  |  | S |  |  |  |  |  |
|  |  | M |  |  |  |  |  |
|  |  | O |  |  |  |  |  |
|  |  | P |  |  |  |  |  |
|  |  | O |  |  |  |  |  |
|  |  | L |  |  |  |  |  |
|  |  | I |  |  |  |  |  |
|  |  | T |  |  |  |  |  |
|  |  | A |  |  |  |  |  |
|  |  | N |  |  |  |  |  |

## Recommendations

**9** Rearrange the words to make recommendations.

a I'd / for / Personally, / a / stay / week
*Personally, I'd stay for a week.*

b are / crowded / The / far / northern / too / beaches
_____ .

c definitely / the / You / try / seafood / should
_____ .

d its / for / wine / It's / famous / festival
_____ .

e the / I / recommend / campsite / wouldn't
_____ .

f really / cathedral / worth / The / seeing / is
_____ .

g wouldn't / taxis / I / use / Personally, / the
_____ .

## Punctuation
### Capital letters

We use a capital letter for:
- people's initials and names, their marital status and job title: *Ms F. Green, Personnel Manager.*
- the names or initials of companies: *International Chemicals, IBM.*
- the names of places: *New Zealand, Park Road.*
- languages, nationalities and religions: *Tom speaks Chinese, a Greek statue, Sue's a Buddhist.*
- days, months, and public holidays: *Christmas Day is on Wednesday the 25th of December.*
- the most important words in titles of books, magazines, films, etc.: *Empire of the Sun.*

**10** Find and correct any mistakes in the sentences.

a I'm meeting ~~p~~ P rofessor Allinton on Tuesday ~~a~~ A fternoon, aren't I?

b Do you know any good japanese restaurants? Our Managing director, Mr Hashimoto, is coming over next week.

c *Twenty thousand leagues under the sea* was written by jules verne.

d What are you doing at easter?

e We went on holiday to turkey and stayed for a few days in istanbul.

f Who directed *sleepless in seattle*?

g jack's birthday's on february 22nd – that's next wednesday.

## Listen and read
### Unusual holidays

**11** a **T3.5** Listen to and/or read the texts about holidays and answer the questions.

1 In which holiday do you stay …
   a underground? _The Legendary Ghan Opal Safari_
   b under the water? _____
   c on a boat? _____
   d in ice? _____

2 Which holidays involve diving?
   _____

3 Which holiday uses a lot of technology?
   _____

4 In which holiday can you drive two types of transport?
   _____

b Listen and/or read again and answer these questions.

1 How many different types of transport are mentioned in the six holidays?
   _____

2 In which holiday do you travel the fastest and the furthest?
   _____

3 Which holidays are only at certain times in the year?
   _____

4 Why are the houses built underground in Coober Pedy?
   _____

5 What can you see from the plane on the 'Final Frontier' holiday?
   _____

6 Do you know your route in advance on the 'Storm Chasing' holiday?
   _____

7 How can you relax on the 'Lapland Adventure Weekend'?
   _____

8 Can you stay at the Jules' Undersea Lodge for more than one night?
   _____

9 Do you need to be able to dive to go on the 'White Shark Heaven' holiday?
   _____

## The Legendary Ghan Opal Safari

This is an extraordinary five-day journey from Adelaide on the south coast to Alice Springs, with an overnight tour to Coober Pedy, where seventy percent of the world's opals are mined. The Ghan is one of Australia's most luxurious trains: you will be travelling across a hostile landscape of desert, salt lakes, mountains and hot springs, but in true comfort whether you travel first class or not.

At Coober Pedy, the temperatures are so extreme (up to 50°C during the day and 0°C at night) that all the houses are built underground as well as the mines. You stay at the Desert Cave Hotel, where the rooms have been cut out of the rock.

**Tours are throughout the year and cost $890.**

## The Final Frontier: 3,400 kph

Journey to the edge of space in a Russian Foxbat jetfighter.

Travel at more than twice the speed of sound, to over 24,000 metres above the Earth. Join those few free spirits that have already experienced this journey to the edge of space. At about thirty-two kilometres above the ground, the curve of the Earth comes dramatically into view.

In the cockpit of a Russian MiG–25 military fighter plane you're aboard the fastest combat aircraft in the world.

*Limited dates.*

**Contact us direct for details and cost.**

## Storm Chasing

Witness spectacular explosive thunderstorms, lightning and tornadoes. Come with us as we follow the storm and get as close as we can, to give you the most exciting experience. Our vans are equipped with the latest storm chasing technology, like our Weather Radar System, In-Motion Satellite Tracking System, and Lightning Display System that shows storms and lightning up to 500 kilometres away. We travel as far as necessary to see the tornadoes: the chase could take you anywhere in Texas, Oklahoma, Kansas or Eastern Colorado.

*Dates between May and July.*

**Ten days for $1,700.**

## Lapland Adventure Weekend

Head up to the frozen north and experience the thrill of a husky sledging expedition. Drive your own team of huskies and stay overnight in a wooden lodge, where you can relax and enjoy a traditional sauna. Also stay in the famous ice hotel, drive a snowmobile, and with luck see the famous northern lights (aurora borealis), a wonderful natural display of green, red and purple lights in the sky. This is a really unforgettable and unique short break.

*Three nights for $2,500.*

**January to April.**

## Luxury Under Water

Jules' Undersea Lodge in Key Largo, Florida was originally built as La Chalupa mobile undersea laboratory, the largest and most technically advanced in the world. The Lodge has been completely remodelled to provide guests with luxury living space for up to six people. The interior has two living chambers, with bedrooms and dining and entertainment facilities. Earn an Aquanaut certificate while enjoying unlimited diving for certified divers, a gourmet dinner prepared by a 'mer-chef', and a gourmet breakfast. If desired, guests may spend several days underwater without surfacing.

**All year round. $295 per night.**

## White Shark Heaven, Mexico

The world's ultimate shark dive and fishing adventure is closer than you think.
For divers, non-divers and tuna fishermen, discover Isla Guadalupe, one of the world's most exciting new Great White dive sites.
Your cage dive and world-class tuna fishing expedition takes you on a five-day live-aboard adventure to the newly discovered and beautiful Isla Guadalupe site off the coast of Mexico. You will have the opportunity to dive by day with Great White Sharks and fish for huge tuna in the hunting grounds of Great Whites and Mako sharks.

**Five-Day Live-Aboard Expeditions: October to November for $2,250.**

## Improve your writing
### Postcards

When writing postcards, we often leave out a lot of words to save space:
- ~~We're~~ having a great time …
- ~~The~~ food is wonderful …

**12** **a** Read the postcard from New York and decide where the words in the box should go. What types of words are usually left out?

| The | there | are | my | is |
|-----|-------|-----|-----|-----|
| We're | We're | We'll | be | |
| The | is | We | | |

Dear Pete and Sarah,

We're
having a great time here in the Big Apple. Weather brilliant – hot and sunny. Spent most of today shopping – fantastic department stores here: credit card's not looking too healthy! Hoping to do some sightseeing tomorrow – Fifth Avenue, Times Square, etc. Nightlife also incredible … nobody seems to go to bed!

Back in a couple of weeks,

love Sue and Joe
xxxx

Mr and Mrs Hall,
3 Park Grove,
Leicester,
England.

**b** Read the postcard from Rome and circle the words which can be left out.

Dear Sam and Julie,

We arrived here a couple of days ago – the hotel is small but comfortable, but the food is not great. We're going on a tour of the whole city tomorrow, then we're planning to try some typical pasta dishes for dinner. We hope your family are all well, we'll see you in September.

Love Mark and Tim

Sam and Julie Foster,
School Cottage,
Broadwood,
Gloucester,
England.

**c** Imagine that you are on holiday. Write a postcard to an English-speaking friend.

...........................................................
...........................................................
...........................................................
...........................................................
...........................................................
...........................................................
...........................................................
...........................................................
...........................................................

## Vocabulary
## Word building

**1** Complete the sentences by changing the word in capitals to the correct form. The words all come from Reading on pages 36 and 37 of the Students' Book.

a  How many ___political___ parties are there in your country? POLITICS

b  My sister has a very strong _____ – she always says what she thinks. PERSON

c  You must be _____ ! How did you know I was going to say that? TELEPATHY

d  Can we pay _____ , please? SEPARATE

e  Did you know that you have exactly the same _____ expressions as your mother? FACE

f  You're going to Paris this weekend, too? What a _____ ! COINCIDE

g  Some people pay _____ prices for designer clothes. BELIEVE

h  There are some _____ between the two paintings, but I don't think it's the same artist. SIMILAR

i  After all the discussion, the council still hasn't come to a _____ about the building work. CONCLUDE

j  My grandmother was a _____ woman: she brought up six children by herself. REMARK

k  I had quite a strict _____ : my parents had quite old-fashioned ideas about how children should behave. BRING

## Present perfect simple

**2** **a** Circle the irregular verbs in the 'snake' and write the past participles below. The last letter of one verb is the first letter of the next.

breaknoweareadrinkeeputearingetellendriveateachithrowin

| | | | | | |
|---|---|---|---|---|---|
| 1 | _broken_ | 7 | _____ | 13 | _____ |
| 2 | _known_ | 8 | _____ | 14 | _____ |
| 3 | _____ | 9 | _____ | 15 | _____ |
| 4 | _____ | 10 | _____ | 16 | _____ |
| 5 | _____ | 11 | _____ | 17 | _____ |
| 6 | _____ | 12 | _____ | 18 | _____ |

**b** Complete the gaps with the correct Present perfect form of the verbs in part a.

1  A:  You've got a lot of books. _Have_ you _read_ them all?
   B:  No! A lot of them are books I _____ from when I was at school.
   A:  Oh – I _____ out all my old books from school.

2  A:  Oh, no! This is the first time I _____ this T-shirt and I _____ it already.
   B:  Let's have a look. Oh, it's only a small hole; no one will see it.

3  A:  Mum! Ben _____ his head on the corner of the table! He's crying!
   B:  Jonathan! How many times _____ I _____ you not to play in here? OK, don't worry, I'm sure he _____ any bones!

4  A:  Sorry, I can't pick you up from the train station. I _____ the car to Alex.
   B:  Are you sure that was a good idea? She _____ never _____ an automatic before!

5  A:  Look – I _____ your photo on our website.
   B:  That's great! How long _____ you _____ how to build websites?

6  A:  Who _____ all the biscuits that were in this tin?
   B:  I don't know, Mum.
   A:  Hmm, and someone _____ all the Coke, too.
   B:  Maybe it was a burglar!

## Present perfect simple and Past simple

3 Read this interview with Zoe, a singer in a pop group, and choose the best verb form.

I = Interviewer    Z = Zoe

I: Well, it's nearly the end of December and your single (a) *was /* has been number 1 all month. You must be very pleased.

Z: Oh yes, of course. (b) *it was / it's been* an incredible year for us – we (c) *already had / 've already had* two number 1 songs this year and we (d) *did / 've done* a tour of the UK.

I: OK, tell us how it all (e) *started / has started.*

Z: We only (f) *formed / have formed* the group in January, and since then we (g) *spent / 've spent* almost every day together. At first, we only (h) *played / have played* other people's songs and we (i) *didn't start / haven't started* writing our own songs until we (j) *found / 've found* our manager, Brian.

I: Uh huh … so when (k) *was / 's been* your first big concert?

Z: Well, that was two months ago, and around the same time Brian (l) *got / 's got* us a recording contract with Sony.

I: Yes, and your album (m) *went / 's gone* to number 3 in the charts the week it was released. So, what's next?

Z: Well, we're working on some new songs and we (n) *just agreed / 've just agreed* to do a US tour next summer.

I: Great! Well, we all wish you the best of luck and thank you for coming on the programme.

4 Six of the sentences below are wrong. Find the mistakes and correct them.

a ~~Have you seen~~ the news last night? *Did you see*

b Carrie's a really close friend – we knew each other for ages.

c Hello, er … sorry, I forgot your name.

d Jeff's never broken a promise before.

e Oh, that's a nice watch. How long did you have it?

f My boss was late for work every day last month.

g Look! It's stopped raining!

h I see your team's in the final. Did they ever win the cup?

i We didn't play tennis together since the summer.

j I can't find my keys – has anyone seen them?

5 a Read this extract from an article called *Famous Mums and Dads* and complete the gaps with the Present perfect simple or Past simple of the verbs in brackets.

'It (1) ___was___ (be) my birthday yesterday: I'm fourteen years old. Some people say I'm lucky but I don't think so. Imagine, in my life I (2) _____ (go) to eight different schools and I (3) _____ (never stay) anywhere long enough to make a best friend. We (4) _____ (live) in so many different houses that I can't remember some of them. In fact, last year we (5) _____ (move) house three times. It's true, there are some good things: I (6) _____ (meet) some really famous people and we (7) _____ (have) some great holidays – I (8) _____ (go) to Disneyland at least four times, but never with mum and dad. When I (9) _____ (be) young, I always (10) _____ (have) a nanny, and she (11) _____ (take) me on holiday. I'm staying with my aunt and uncle at the moment because my dad's making a film in France and my mum (12) _____ (go) to Los Angeles.'

b [T4.1] Listen and check.

## Time words with the Present perfect

6 Rearrange the words to make sentences.

a haven't / my / yet / homework / I / done
   I haven't done my homework yet.

b film / I / started / the / already / has / think
   _____ .

c Mariel / of / come / hospital / yet / Has / out ?
   _____ .

d many / week / have / shopping / you / this / How / been / times ?
   _____ .

e my / lived / all / here / I've / life
   _____ .

f has / friend / got / My / just / engaged / best
   _____ .

g on / ever / television / you / appeared / Have ?
   _____ .

**7 a** Match a sentence in column A with a response in column B. Then put the time words in brackets in the right place in the responses.

**A**

1 ☐ h Have you seen Ed this afternoon?

2 ☐ You look great.

3 ☐ Do you want some lunch?

4 ☐ What did you think of the DVD I lent you?

5 ☐ Do you know Susie?

6 ☐ Have you ever tried chilli prawns?

7 ☐ Why haven't you got any money?

8 ☐ Is Dina on holiday?

**B**

a Yes, we've met. (already)

_____

b Well, I've had to pay a lot of bills. (this month)

_____

c No, I've been able to eat chilli. (never)

_____

d Thanks, I've come back from holiday. (just)

_____

e No thanks, I've had a sandwich. (already)

_____

f I haven't had time to watch it. (yet)

_____

g No, she's been off sick. (all week)

_____

h No, he hasn't come back from lunch. (yet)
*No, he hasn't come back from lunch yet.*

**b** T4.2 Listen and check.

## Vocabulary
### Describing life events

**8** Complete the phrases in the article with the correct verbs.

# From Bottom of the Class to Businesswoman of the Year

At the age of sixty, Tessa Daley, director of Newsgroup Publishing, has it all: she has (a) b *ecome* so successful that she seems to be on TV or in the papers every week, and she has (b) m_____ more money than most of us could dream of. But this is the woman who (c) f_____ all her exams and (d) l_____ school with no qualifications.

'I hated school and couldn't wait to get away and (e) s_____ work. I (f) g_____ a job at a local newsagent's. I loved working there because I could read all the magazines, but unfortunately I was asked to leave two weeks later – for reading magazines and forgetting to serve the customers!'

One of the customers was Simon, a good-looking journalist, who she (g) f_____ in love with. They (h) g_____ engaged six weeks after the first meeting, then (i) g_____ married at the end of that year. Tessa devoted the next sixteen years of her life to being a wife and (j) b_____ up her children. Simon (k) c_____ jobs a lot during those years, and the family (l) m_____ house several times. The disruption had a disastrous effect on the marriage and they (m) s_____ up when the oldest child was fifteen.

'After I (n) g_____ divorced there was a big gap in my life and I didn't know what to do. My daughter persuaded me to go to university to (o) d_____ media studies.' Tessa worked hard and (p) p_____ her exams with the best grades in her year. 'The day I (q) g_____ my degree was the proudest day of my life.'

Tessa has just launched a new magazine and is busier than ever: she has no plans to retire yet!

## *for, since* and *ago* and Present perfect continuous

**9** Complete the sentences with the Present perfect continuous of the verbs in the box.

| cry | go | phone | not work | rain |
| read | talk | use | | |

a You _'ve been reading_ that book for ages – haven't you finished it yet?

b My brother _____ a lot recently about moving to Canada, but I don't know if he will.

c We _____ the same recipe for our famous 'Chocolotti' biscuits for the last fifty years, and it's still a secret.

d Joseph _____ to evening classes since the summer, but he still can't say 'What's your name?' in Russian!

e _____ Kerry _____ ? Do you know what's wrong?

f I _____ here very long – do you know where the stationery cupboard is?

g Excuse me, Marcia, a reporter from *Vanity Fair* _____ all morning – could you speak to her now?

h How long _____ it _____ ? I haven't got an umbrella with me.

**10** Finish the sentences with the words in brackets and *for, since* or *ago*.

a Jo's had toothache ___for three days___ . (three days)

b Frankie last went to the dentist _____ . (six months)

c I started going jogging _____ . (a year)

d Jane's been feeling sick _____ . (last night)

e Pete's been on a diet _____ . (two weeks)

f I haven't done any exercise _____ . (months)

g I've been doing aerobics _____ . (this time last year)

h She hasn't been feeling well _____ . (her operation)

**11** Choose the best verb form in the sentences.

a I*'ve been knowing* / *'ve known* Susan for about five years.

b Mum had to take Tim to the dentist because he*'s been breaking* / *'s broken* his tooth.

c My husband*'s been having* / *'s had* his mobile phone for a week and it's already broken.

d I hope Karen rings soon because Rick*'s been waiting* / *'s waited* by the phone for hours.

e We*'ve been going* / *'ve gone* to the new sports centre since June. Why don't you come and try it?

f Giuseppina's English is getting much better. She*'s been practising* / *'s practised* a lot recently.

g You look much slimmer. Have you *been dieting* / *dieted*?

h John's boss *has been deciding* / *has decided* to have a holiday next month.

i Goodbye and thanks. We*'ve really been enjoying* / *'ve really enjoyed* this evening.

# Vocabulary booster
## Describing people

**12** **a** Put the phrases from the box into the correct category.

| | | |
|---|---|---|
| ~~good-looking~~ | ~~creative~~ | glasses |
| stubborn | smartly | a lot of jewellery |
| stunning | over sixty | a good figure |
| casually | attractive | witty |
| a lot of style | middle-aged | in his teens |
| a lovely smile | good dress sense | chatty |
| serious | scruffily | in her late thirties |
| good fun | a friendly face | the same age as me |
| in his mid forties | a few wrinkles | in her early twenties |

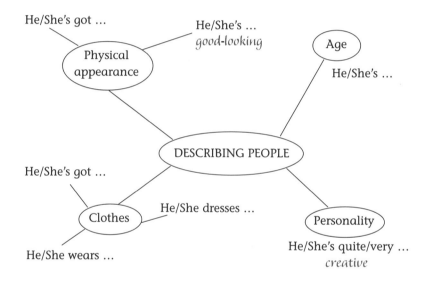

He/She's got …

He/She's …
*good-looking*

Age

He/She's …

**Physical appearance**

DESCRIBING PEOPLE

He/She's got …

He/She dresses …

Clothes

Personality

He/She wears …

He/She's quite/very …
*creative*

**b** **T4.3** Listen and repeat the phrases.

**c** Put the phrases about age in the box in order from the youngest to the oldest.

_____

**d** Complete these sentences about yourself.

1 I'm quite _____ .

2 I dress _____ .

3 I haven't got any _____ .

4 I'm very _____ .

5 I wear _____ .

6 I don't wear _____ .

7 I'm not very _____ .

8 I've got _____ .

# Pronunciation
## /ɪ/, /iː/, /aɪ/ and /eɪ/

> **LOOK!**
>
> Compare these three sounds:
>
> | /ɪ/ | sixty | script |
> |---|---|---|
> | | /ɪ/ | /ɪ/ |
> | /iː/ | me | screen |
> | | /iː/ | /iː/ |
> | /aɪ/ | quite | signed |
> | | /aɪ/ | /aɪ/ |
> | /eɪ/ | face | break |
> | | /eɪ/ | /eɪ/ |

**13** **a** **T4.4** Listen to the words in the box (or say them aloud) and complete the table.

| | | | |
|---|---|---|---|
| ~~teen~~ | recent | accl**ai**m | **i**dol |
| h**igh**lights | g**ui**tar | rel**a**tionship |
| st**y**le | m**e**dia | **i**mage | bl**a**me |
| sm**i**le | w**i**tty | cr**i**tic | f**ea**ture |
| middle-**a**ged | | | |

| /ɪ/ | /iː/ | /aɪ/ | /eɪ/ |
|---|---|---|---|
| | *teen* | | |
| | | | |
| | | | |

**b** **T4.5** Listen to these phrases and repeat them, or say them aloud.

1 He's a teen idol.
2 There was a lot of media attention.
3 She's very witty and she's got a lovely smile.
4 The relationship ended suddenly.
5 She's got a lot of style.
6 They're both middle-aged.
7 His first feature film won critical acclaim
8 In his recent work he has a different image.

## Listen and read
### Johnny Depp

**Johnny Depp**

Born: June 9, 1963
Where: Owensboro, Kentucky

**14** a ⬤**T4.6** Listen to and/or read the biography of film star Johnny Depp and put the following life events in order.

☐ He became a teen idol.

☐ He directed a film.

☐ He got married for the second time.

☐ He had a job selling pens over the phone.

☐ He met an actor who persuaded him to try acting.

☐ He played a part in a horror film.

☐ 1 He played the guitar in a band.

☐ He was voted one of the 'beautiful people'.

Rare among American actors, Depp has made a name for himself effortlessly switching between mainstream Hollywood movies and more 'out of the ordinary' projects. Talking about his choice of roles, he once said: 'With any part you play, there is a certain amount of yourself in it. There has to be, otherwise it's not acting. It's lying.' Highlights of a richly diverse career include *Edward Scissorhands*, *Sleepy Hollow* and *Pirates of the Caribbean*.

Depp dropped out of school at sixteen to concentrate on a career in music, playing the guitar (he played with more than twenty bands). However, his musical career failed to take off, and he found himself selling pens over the phone to pay the bills. His lucky break came when makeup artist Lori Allison, to whom he was briefly married, introduced him to Nicolas Cage. Although at first they did not like each other, they later became good friends and Cage persuaded him to

try acting. Depp signed on with Cage's agent, and made his feature film debut in Wes Craven's horror film *Nightmare on Elm Street*, in which the character he played was eaten by his bed. After that he had his first screen leading role in *Private Resort*.

Depp went on to achieve teen idol status in the TV series *21 Jump Street*, but after four seasons, he wanted out, with the hope of making the transition to the big screen. He starred in *Cry-Baby*, followed by Tim Burton's *Edward Scissorhands*, after which he went on to win considerable critical acclaim in *Ed Wood*, a reunion with Burton. Depp made his feature directorial debut with *The Brave* in 1997, a film he also co-wrote and starred in. Premiering at the Cannes Film Festival, the film also featured Marlon Brando, but earned mostly negative reviews, with most critics blaming its weak script. *Sleepy Hollow* teamed him with director Burton yet again, before he starred in Ted

Demme's *Blow*, and appeared in the thriller *From Hell*, about Jack the Ripper.

Off screen, his good looks and 'bad boy' image (he was once arrested for attacking intrusive paparazzi with a wooden plank) have earned him a lot of media attention. He was voted one of the fifty most beautiful people in the world by *People* magazine in 1996. He has also had his fair share of celebrity romances; when his engagement to *Edward Scissorhands* co-star Winona Ryder ended, he had a tattoo (one of at least eight), which said 'Winona Forever', altered by laser to get rid of the last two letters of her name. His relationship with model Kate Moss also ended abruptly in 1998, when he started dating French singer-actress Vanessa Paradis. They are now married and have two children, Lily-Rose Melody and Jack. More recent work has included *Pirates of the Caribbean* with Geoffrey Rush and *Once Upon a Time in Mexico*.

b Listen and/or read again and answer the questions.

1 Why is Johnny Depp a 'rare' actor?

_____ .

2 What does he describe as 'lying'?

_____ .

3 Why did he get a job selling pens over the phone?

_____ .

4 Why has Nicholas Cage been important in his career?

_____ .

5 What was strange about his first film role?

_____ .

6 Who was he popular with in *21 Jump Street*?

_____ .

7 What was his involvement in *The Brave*?

_____ .

8 How many films has he made with director Tim Burton?

_____ .

9 Has he still got the tattoo of Winona Ryder's name?

_____ .

10 Who was his co-star in *Pirates of the Caribbean*?

_____ .

## Wordspot
### take

**15** Match a sentence beginning in A with an ending in B.

**A**

a | 9 | Come in and take
b | | Could you take care
c | | The photographer took
d | | You really take
e | | Dario's taking me
f | | This is the third time Yuki's taken her
g | | Do you want me to take
h | | It's OK, I can take a later
i | | I've lost lots of weight since I took
j | | How can you afford to take
k | | We've been asked to take
l | | Do you always take a lot of

**B**

1 up cycling.
2 out for a romantic meal tonight.
3 driving test.
4 part in a national health survey.
5 of my goldfish while I'm away?
6 train if I miss this one.
7 some fantastic pictures at the wedding.
8 over the driving now? You look tired.
9 off those wet shoes.
10 notes during the lesson?
11 after your father – you've got his smile.
12 three holidays a year?

## Improve your writing
### Punctuation: commas

LOOK!

We put a comma (,) in a sentence to show a short pause.

In a list, we use a comma instead of *and* or *or*:
- *He lived in France, Italy, Belgium and Spain.*

When we join two short sentences with a conjunction, e.g. *and*, *but* or *so*, we often use a comma before the conjunction:
- *He moved to France, but he never forgot his friends in England.*

If the sentence is short, a comma is not always necessary:
- *He loved Paris but I didn't.*

Notice where we put the commas in direct speech:
- *'I'll buy the tickets,' he said.*
- *She said, 'It's okay, I've got lots of money.'*

**16** **a** Insert commas where necessary.

1 I'm not very keen on jazz blues or rock music.
2 Steve practises his guitar every day and has guitar lessons twice a week.
3 I don't know much about the Beatles but I like their music a lot.
4 I like going to rock concerts but the tickets can be really expensive so I don't go often.
5 Jorge said 'You can borrow my guitar.'
6 'Come on' Paddy said 'or we'll be late.'
7 I can get tickets for the 12th 13th or 15th January.
8 The music was very loud but quite good.

**b** In the following extract Bob Geldof, a famous rock star, talks about his meeting with Mother Teresa of Calcutta. Read the text and insert commas where necessary.

We sat in the airport till Mother Teresa came in. I felt hot tired and a bit nervous. I wanted to kiss her when I met her but she didn't let me. She told me about her work in Ethiopia. She and her sisters took care of sick people and homeless children. I wanted to help them and I told her about my music.
Then I said 'I'll give a concert in India for you.'
'No. God will give us what we need.' She turned to one of the important people nearby.
'I saw two big old palaces in the city' she said. 'Will you give me them for my homeless children?'
'I'm not sure about palaces but we can find you a house.'
'Two houses' said Mother Teresa.
'Two houses.'
I understood that Mother Teresa could ask for anything and she would get it. She was all goodness. She wanted nothing for herself. Then she took my hand and said 'I can do something you can't do and you can do something I can't do but we both have to do it.

## Vocabulary
### Prepositions

**1** Choose the correct alternative in each sentence. The phrases come from the psychometric test on pages 48 and 49 of the Students' Book.

---

### Office Survival skills

**Boring job? Here are ten tips on how to get through the week.**

**1** Put your boss in a good mood on Monday morning: find *about* / *out* what his/her favourite chocolates are and leave some on his/her desk.

**2** Always look as if you're concentrating *on* / *in* your work when the boss walks past.

**3** Distract your colleagues *off* / *from* their work by sending them funny e-mails.

**4** Make sure that you always leave the office at lunchtime so that you can switch *out* / *off* from work for a while.

**5** If your boss asks you to work late, tell him / her you have important plans *for* / *at* the evening which you can't possibly cancel.

**6** Find an interesting course and persuade your boss to pay *for* / *to* you to do it as part of your professional development.

**7** If your boss asks you to do some extra photocopying, say that you have to get on *at* / *with* some work for an important client.

**8** Don't waste time looking *back* / *behind* at your mistakes – just hope that no one notices them.

**9** Always remember that this job may lead *to* / *on* something better in the future.

**10** If you've really had enough by Friday lunchtime, tell your boss that something urgent has come *on* / *up* at home and you've got to leave early.

---

## Vocabulary
### Nouns and adjectives

**2** Complete the gaps with a noun or adjective from the table on page 49 of the Students' Book.

a  The advertising campaign was a great __happy__ : sales figures are looking very good.

b  She's really good at her job but she doesn't have much _____ in herself.

c  Sophie didn't get that promotion she wanted, but she's _____ not to get upset about it.

d  This is a very _____ project: do you really think we can complete it in time?

e  Jon's ideas for the website are practical, but they're not very _____ – I'd like to try a more creative designer.

f  I want the team to understand the _____ of this agreement for the future of the company.

g  Please don't insult my _____ – I know why we lost the contract, and I know who was to blame.

h  I'm afraid we all have to accept the _____ of redundancies if things don't start to improve.

### *will* and *won't*

**3** Complete the sentences with *will* or *won't* and a verb from the box.

| agree | be | be ready | come | get | like | need |
|---|---|---|---|---|---|---|
| pass | send | take | | | | |

a  I need these shoes on Saturday. __Will they be ready__ (they) by then?

b  We _____ to order the flowers at least two weeks before the wedding.

c  _____ (you) late tonight?

d  I don't think you should buy Mum those gloves, she _____ them.

e  So, the exam's in June. When _____ (they) us the results?

f  Don't forget to take a sweater: I expect it _____ cold later.

g  Stop worrying about the exam – you _____ easily.

h  Why do you want to leave so early? It _____ very long to get there.

## going to

4 Complete the conversations with the correct form of *going to* and a suitable verb where necessary. (Short answers may be possible.)

a A: It's my eighteenth birthday in June.
  B: *Are you going to have* a party?
  A: I haven't decided yet.

b A: My brother's just heard that he's lost his job.
  B: Oh, no! What _____ ?
  A: I think he's planning to travel for a while.

c A: Are you really going to give up smoking?
  B: Yes, _____ .
     I threw my last packet of cigarettes away yesterday.

d A: Have you got any plans for the weekend?
  B: Well, David and I _____ a film on Sunday night.
  A: Oh, which one?

e A: Are you nervous about making a speech at the wedding?
  B: Yes, but I _____ about it any more.
  A: No – thinking about it will only make you more nervous.

f A: Lisa's really in love with Alain, isn't she?
  B: _____ him?
  A: I hope so. He'd be the perfect husband for her.

g A: I heard that the council have bought that land behind the cinema to build on.
  B: Oh, really? What _____ there?
  A: A new shopping mall, I think.

h A: Are you and Annie going to have a holiday this year?
  B: No, _____ . We haven't got any money.

## Present continuous for future arrangements

5 Look at the diaries and use the prompts to complete the dialogues on the next page.

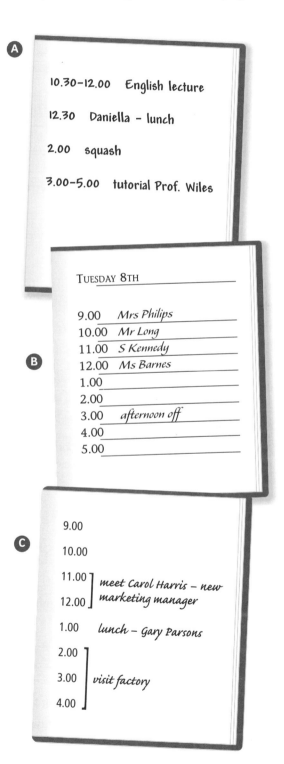

**A**

10.30–12.00   English lecture

12.30   Daniella – lunch

2.00   squash

3.00–5.00   tutorial Prof. Wiles

**B**

TUESDAY 8TH _____

9.00   Mrs Philips _____
10.00   Mr Long _____
11.00   S Kennedy _____
12.00   Ms Barnes _____
1.00   _____
2.00   _____
3.00   afternoon off _____
4.00   _____
5.00   _____

**C**

9.00

10.00

11.00 ⎤ meet Carol Harris – new
12.00 ⎦ marketing manager

1.00   lunch – Gary Parsons

2.00 ⎤
3.00 ⎬ visit factory
4.00 ⎦

**Diary A**

A: Hi Josh. Can we meet some time today to talk about the English assignment?

B: Well, I'm quite busy. I / go / to a lecture this morning and I / meet / Daniella for lunch.

(a) *I'm going to a lecture this morning and I'm meeting Daniella for lunch.*

A: What / you / do in the afternoon?

(b) _____

_____

B: Well, I / play / squash until 3.00, then I've got a tutorial.

(c) _____

_____

you / do / anything in the evening? I'm free then.

(d) _____

_____

A: OK. That's great. See you this evening, then.

**Diary B**

A: Hello, Mr Haines' surgery.

B: Yes, hello. Could I see the dentist today? I've got terrible toothache.

A: Well, he / see / patients all morning.

(e) _____

_____

B: Um ... what about the afternoon?

A: No, I'm afraid he / have / the afternoon off. Actually, he could fit you in at one o'clock.

(f) _____

_____

B: Oh, thank you very much.

**Diary C**

A: Yes, Mr Riley?

B: Ah, Celia, what time / I / have / lunch with Gary Parsons?

(g) _____

_____

A: One o'clock.

B: Well, could you call him and make it a bit later?

A: That's not really possible. you / leave / at two to visit the factory in Stanmore.

(h) _____

_____

B: Oh yes, of course.

# Other ways of talking about the future

**6** Use the prompts to make complete sentences in the dialogues.

a A: My nephew Justin's leaving school in July.

B: Oh, what / he / want / do / after that ?
*Oh, what does he want to do after that?*

b A: What time are your grandparents coming?

B: They / due / arrive / at about six.

_____

c A: I'm going to spend the summer in Turkey.

B: Really? Where / you / planning / stay ?

_____

d A: I hear you've bought a new house.

B: Yes, we / hoping / move / next month.

_____

e A: Jeannie looks a bit worried.

B: I know, she / about / take / her driving test.

_____

f A: What are you going to do with the money you won in the lottery?

B: Well, I / thinking / buy / a new car with some of it.

_____

# Pronunciation

/ɒ/ **and** /əʊ/

> Compare these sounds:
> /ɒ/    dog, lot
> /əʊ/   note, wrote

**7** a **T5.1** Listen to the words in the box (or say them aloud) and complete the table.

| don't go got home hope job know |
|---|
| lost phone want wasn't watch what |
| won won't |

| /ɒ/ | /əʊ/ |
|---|---|
|  | don't |
|  |  |
|  |  |

**b** 〔T5.2〕 Listen and write the missing words. Then repeat the sentences.

1  I _hope_ hope you _won't_ won't get ___lost___ .

2  I _____ to _____ _____ now.

3  Do you _____ why Petra _____ her _____ ?

4  That _____ _____ I said.

5  We _____ _____ the results until tomorrow.

6  We _____ _____ too late to _____ you.

7  Can you _____ the baby for a minute? I _____ be long.

8  I _____ _____ who _____ the competition.

9  I _____ the hotel _____ too expensive.

10  _____ _____ me before nine – I _____ to _____ the news.

## Vocabulary booster
## Jobs

**8** **a** Choose a word from the box to complete the name of each job below.

| | |
|---|---|
| administrator | agent |
| attendant | designer |
| gardener | guard |
| instructor | ~~manager~~ |
| officer | presenter |
| representative | secretary |
| technician | therapist |

1  assistant _manager_

2  travel _____

3  landscape _____

4  laboratory _____

5  security _____

6  graphic _____

7  fitness _____

8  flight _____

9  television _____

10  sales _____

11  beauty _____

12  press _____

13  office _____

14  legal _____

**b** 〔T5.3〕 Listen and check. Then practise saying the jobs.

**c** Complete the adverts with the jobs in part a.

1  Leading window manufacturer seeks __sales representative__ for Central Coast area. Excellent commission rates.

2  NEW CITY CENTRE GYM SEEKS _____ . FLEXIBLE HOURS, VERY GOOD RATES OF PAY.

3  City Parks require _____ for major development project in Botanical Gardens.

4  _____ required for busy salon. Must be experienced in facial/body treatments.

5  Train to be a _____ . TV Pro has trained and placed many household names. Excellent reputation in the industry.

6  Leading law firm is seeking an experienced _____ to work with the senior partner. Word processing skills essential.

7  Small design firm requires _____ . Expert in Quark, Photoshop and Illustrator.

8  _____ required for furniture warehouse. Must have own transport. Hours: 10 p.m.–7 a.m.

9  Large pharmaceutical company seeks _____ to assist with testing of new medicines.

10  Interested in travel? Good people skills? Qualify as a _____ in six months on our intensive course. Call now for an application form.

11  _____ required for busy video store. Small, friendly staff. Excellent conditions.

12  YOUNG AIRLINE IS NOW RECRUITING _____ FOR NEW ROUTES ACROSS ASIA.

13  _____ required for large tobacco company. Must have good communication skills and experience of dealing with the media.

14  _____ needed for expanding construction company. Duties include admin and accounts. Good telephone manner essential.

## Vocabulary
### Work

**9** Replace the definition in bold with a phrase from Vocabulary on page 51 of the Students' Book.

a Anna has **passed a lot of examinations** but she doesn't have any practical experience.
  *a lot of qualifications*

b Scott didn't get the security guard job – they said he wasn't **strong and healthy** enough.
  _____

c The job sounds interesting, but I don't want to **start very early and finish late**.
  _____

d I left the company because the work was boring and **they didn't pay much**.
  _____

e You're so **good at producing new or interesting ideas** – have you ever thought of going into the fashion industry?
  _____

f My parents want me to be a teacher because it's **a job which I'm not likely to lose**.
  _____

g I thought there would be **going to different places** in journalism, but I was wrong.
  _____

h Wouldn't you like to do something more **difficult in an interesting or enjoyable way** than working in a café?
  _____

i The problem with my boss is he has no **ability to deal with people**.
  _____

j Your job sounds **as if it makes you worry a lot**.
  _____

k Keira wants the promotion, but she doesn't really want the **duty to be in charge and make decisions** that goes with it.
  _____

## Listen and read
### Unusual lifestyles

**10** a **T5.4** Four people are talking about their lifestyles. Listen to and/or read the texts. What are their jobs?

1 Gemma is a/an _____
2 Raoul is a/an _____
3 Frank is a/an _____
4 Megan a/an _____

*Gemma*
*'I absolutely love music and listen to it all the time, even when I go jogging. Of course I have to look after my voice. I do exercises for three hours every day and I take lots of vitamin C. If I get a sore throat I go straight to bed and rest. I usually try to get at least eight hours sleep a night anyway. ... As for my job – you really can't be shy in this kind of work, and you have to be very patient because sometimes we practise for hours before we get it right. When we're on tour, we work for several weeks with no breaks and you can get really tired. For relaxation, whenever I get a holiday, I go straight to a sunny beach, but the thing I enjoy the most is the great feeling you get from a live audience.'*

Raoul
'Well, my work's really quite stressful. Most people think you spend your day chopping vegetables and stirring soup, but it's not that simple. You have to be really careful with the food and keep everything very clean. The big problem is my boss – he shouts at me all the time – even, for example, if I forget to wash up one plate – I just can't do anything right sometimes. Actually, I'm hoping to find a new job soon because I don't get much time off. I'd like to have more weekends free, to see friends and to spend more time with my two little boys. You know it's strange spending all day with food – when I go home I just want to eat a sandwich or a bag of chips and I'm terribly critical when I eat in a restaurant.'

**Frank**

'Well, I first got interested because I loved doing them so much myself – I used to do at least one every day. I suppose I've got the right kind of mind really – I enjoy playing around with puzzles, especially word puzzles. So I sent a couple in to a local newspaper and was really surprised when they asked me for more. I suppose it is a strange way to spend your day – surrounded by dictionaries and books, but it's great that I can organise my own time, so I try to finish by two and then I can take my dog for a walk. It's very satisfying though – I love the feeling after I've thought of the final clue, and it all fits together. It's also really nice when people write to me and thank me. Funny really, because I'm just doing what I like.'

**Megan**

*People sometimes ask me if I forget which country I'm in or what time of day it is, but I guess I've got used to it. Last week I was in London and tomorrow I'm going to Hong Kong. I'm based in Bahrain, and I have a small apartment there, although I sometimes don't spend more than seven or eight days a month there. The thing I like most about my job is the contact with the people from different cultures: the idea that it's a glamorous job is a bit of a cliché – you spend a lot of your time handing out food and drinks and clearing up people's rubbish. I certainly don't feel very glamorous at two in the morning! Actually, there are a lot of things that we're trained to do that people don't realise – like fight fires, deliver babies, survive in the desert or ocean.*

---

**b  Listen to or read the texts again. Are these statements true (T) or false (F)?**

1  Gemma has to keep fit.  ___T___

2  The most tiring part of Gemma's job is when she's on tour. _____

3  Gemma hates performing live. _____

4  Raoul's boss is quite easy going. _____

5  Raoul works a lot at weekends. _____

6  Raoul doesn't spend much time cooking at home. _____

7  Frank started writing crossword puzzles for a newspaper. _____

8  Frank uses a lot of reference material for his job. _____

9  Frank has to work long hours. _____

10  Megan spends more time in Bahrain than overseas. _____

11  Megan thinks her job is glamorous. _____

12  Megan's training was quite varied. _____

# Future clauses with *if*, *when*, etc.

**11** Match a question from A with answer from B. Then complete the answers with the correct form of a verb from the box.

| be   come   find   ~~finish~~   get   receive |

**A**
a  [4]  What time do you think you'll be home?
b  [ ]  Can you phone your sister tonight?
c  [ ]  When can I expect to get the results?
d  [ ]  Have you finished writing those invitations?
e  [ ]  Is Gary coming to the party?
f  [ ]  Have you go the new Dido CD?

**B**
1  He'll try to come if he _____ free.
2  Not yet. I'll finish them once I _____ my pen.
3  OK, I'll call her as soon as I _____ home.
4  I'll be on the six o'clock train unless the meeting _finishes_ late.
5  Yes, it's great. I'll play it for you when you _____ over on Saturday.
6  I don't know exactly – we'll post them to you when we _____ them.

## 12 Look at the sentences and make one complete sentence, using the word in bold.

a You'll be in Madrid again. Phone me then. **when**

Phone me *when you're in Madrid again.*

b It's going to get dark soon. Let's stop now. **before**

Let's stop _____ .

c I'm moving house next week. Then I'll give you my phone number. **after**

I'll give _____ .

d That film will come out soon. I'd like to see it then.

**as soon as**

I'd like _____ .

e Maurizio'll finish university soon. He hopes to get a job then. **once**

Maurizio hopes _____

_____ .

f The taxi'll come in a few minutes. I'll wait with you.

**until**

I'll wait _____ .

g You could take the 9.00 a.m. flight. Then you'll be here by lunchtime. **if**

You'll _____ .

h Come out of the station. You'll see the bus stop on your right. **when**

You'll _____ .

i You may want to go somewhere else. If not, I'll book a table at the Wharf Bistro. **unless**

I'll _____

_____ .

## Punctuation
### Apostrophes

LOOK!

We use apostrophes:
- to show a missing letter or letters: *I am – I'm, He has – He's.*
- to show possession with nouns: *Robin's pen.*

Notice:
- *the girl's mother* = one girl.
  *the girls' mother* = more than one girl.
- With irregular plurals, the apostrophe goes before the *-s*: *the children's game.*
- We don't use apostrophes with possessive pronouns and adjectives: *hers, its, ours, theirs.*

## 13 Insert an apostrophe where necessary in these sentences.

a I read your pen friends letter – she sounds really nice.
b This is the boys bedroom. Theyre both at school at the moment.
c Its a nice day, isnt it?
d Whose is this? I think its hers.
e Whos that in reception?
f The companys lost all its best designers.
g Hes leaving in a years time.
h Shes got five years experience in advertising.
i Have a seat – I wont be a minute.
j Well be back by nine, so therell be time to have some supper.
k I cant come with you – Ive got all my students exams to mark – thats 25 papers!

## Improve your writing
### A letter of reference

## 14 a When Louisa Barry applied for a job through *Horizons Unlimited*, she asked two people to write her a letter of reference. Look at the two letters. Which is:

1 ☐ an employment reference?
2 ☐ a character reference?

**A**

20 April 2004

To whom it may concern,

I confirm that Louisa Barry has been (1) ___employed___ as a personal assistant with this organisation for the last three years, and is (2) _____ €35,000 per annum.

The job of personal assistant carries the following (3) _____ : dealing with all correspondence and telephone calls, organising meetings, conferences and business trips, preparing presentations and reports. Louisa has excellent computer (4) _____ and a very good telephone manner. Her knowledge of French was a real (5) _____ when dealing with our Paris office. She is also extremely reliable and hard working.

I would certainly re-employ Louisa as I consider her to have been a valuable member of the company, who consistently (6) _____ good results.

Yours faithfully,

*Jason Holmes*

Jason Holmes

**B**

15 April 2004

To whom it may concern,

I (7) _____ that I have known Louisa Barry for six years. We first met when she attended a Spanish course that I was teaching, and she has (8) _____ become a family friend.

(9) _____ a student of Spanish, Louisa excelled: she took every opportunity to practise in the classroom, and learnt quickly from her mistakes. She has an extensive Spanish vocabulary, and her pronunciation is very good. As a friend of the family, Louisa has always been kind and thoughtful: she has helped me patiently with computer problems on (10) _____ occasions, and has offered to look after my three children when their nanny was not available.

If you require any (11) _____ information, please do not (12) _____ to contact me.

Yours faithfully,

M. Cortes

b   Complete the gaps in the letters with the words in the box.

| | | | | |
|---|---|---|---|---|
| achieved | As | asset | confirm | ~~employed~~ |
| further | hesitate | numerous | paid | |
| responsibilities | since | skills | | |

## Real life
## A formal telephone call

15 a   You are phoning Mrs Leeson, at Henderson Insurance. If you can't speak to her personally, you need her to phone you back. Complete the dialogue with suitable questions and responses.

A:   Good afternoon, Henderson Insurance, Pam speaking. How can I help?

B:   Good afternoon, could (1) _I speak to Mrs Leeson_ , please?

A:   Just a moment, I'll put you through.

C:   Hello, Mrs Leeson's office, Sandy speaking.

B:   Hello, could (2) _____ ?

C:   I'll just see if she's available. Can I ask who's calling?

B:   (3) _____

C:   One moment, please (pause). Hello, I'm afraid she's not in the office at the moment. Would you like her to call you back?

B:   (4) _____ .

C:   Can I take your number?

B:   (5) _____ .

C:   Right, I'll get her to call you back as soon as she comes in.

B:   (6) _____ .

C:   Goodbye.

b   You are phoning International School to find out information about their English courses for executives. Write the message you would leave on the answering machine.

Answering machine message:
This is the International School answering service. We're sorry there's no one available to take your call. Please leave your message after the tone. If you would like information about courses, please leave your name and address and we'll send you our brochure. Thank you. (*tone*)

_____

_____

_____

_____

c   **T5.5**   Listen to some possible answers for part a and b.

d   **T5.6**   Now try to respond in the spaces on the recording, without looking at your book.

You hear:                    You say:

Good afternoon, Henderson Insurance, Pam speaking. How can I help?

*Good afternoon, could I speak to Mrs Leeson, please?*

## Vocabulary
## TV and radio

**1** Answer the questions using a word from page 60 of the Students' Book.

a Which **A** is used to tell people about a product or a service? _advert_

b Which **C** is a short film where the characters and places are drawings? _____

c Which **CM** keeps you guessing until the last scene? _____

d Which **D** contains factual information about something? _____

e Which **TN** gives you up-to-date information on the traffic conditions? _____

f On which **GS** do people compete for prizes? _____

g Which **LN** tells you what's been happening in your area of the country? _____

h On which **P-I** can people give opinions or ask for advice? _____

i Which **RS** is about ordinary people in unusual or challenging situations? _____

j Which **S-C** is a series of amusing stories about the same set of characters? _____

k Which **SO** is a continuing story about the daily lives of a group of people? _____

l Which **SC** lets you watch highlights of games, races and matches? _____

## -ed/-ing adjectives

**2 a** Complete these letters to a TV magazine with the adjectives in the box.

| boring | confused | ~~convincing~~ | shocked | pleased |
| disappointing | upsetting | disappointed | interesting |

Well done Channel 10 for the brilliant series
*City Mysteries.* The characters were really
(1) _convincing_ and the stories were certainly never
(2) _____ . I was so
(3) _____ when it
finished. Are there plans for
a new series?

I'm rather (4) _____ about ABC's policy on not showing violence before 9 p.m. I watched *The Precinct* at 8.30 p.m. last Thursday and was (5) _____ at the amount of violence shown. My ten-year-old daughter, who was watching with me, found it quite (6) _____ .

I was really (7) _____ when I saw that *Celebrity Spot* was back on SBS. I always look forward to the programme because it has such (8) _____ guests. However, last Friday's show was very (9) _____ – the interviewer asked such stupid questions and hardly gave Mel B a chance to speak!

**b** [T6.1] Listen and check.

**3** Complete the sentences with the correct form of the adjectives in the box.

| amusing / amused | annoying / annoyed |
| depressing / depressed | surprising / ~~surprised~~ |
| frustrating / frustrated | tiring / tired |
| worrying / worried | embarrassing / embarrassed |

a We're very _surprised_ to hear that Ann and Tom are getting married. We didn't think she liked him!

b It was so _____ . Kim's brother came up to talk to me at the party and I didn't recognise him!

c Sandra got very _____ with Geri for being late for another meeting.

d My gran's cat died last week. She's really _____ .

e I've had such a _____ day – I need to sit down and put my feet up.

f Don't look so _____ your flight's not until 6.30, you've got plenty of time.

g I don't find Bob's jokes at all _____ .

h I've had a very _____ shopping trip: I couldn't find anything I liked.

# Prepositions after adjectives

**4** **a** Look at the extracts from the *Longman Dictionary of Contemporary English* to find the prepositions which follow the adjectives below.

> **bored** /bɔːd/ *adj* tired and impatient because you do not think something is interesting, or because you have nothing to do: *Children easily get bored.*| **[+ with]** *I'm bored with the same old routine day after day.*
>
> **con·fused** /kənˈfjuːzd/ *adj* unable to understand clearly what someone is saying or what is happening: *I am totally confused. Could you explain that again?*| **[+ about]** *If you are confused about anything, phone my office.*
>
> **de·pressed** /dɪˈprest/ *adj* a) feeling very unhappy: *She felt lonely and depressed.*| **[+ about]** *Carter seemed depressed about the situation.*
>
> **dis·ap·point·ed** /ˌdɪsəˈpɔɪntɪd/ *adj* sad because something you hoped for did not happen, or because someone or something was not as good as expected: *Dad seemed more disappointed than angry.*| **[+ about]** *Nathan's really disappointed about not being able to go.*
>
> **em·bar·rassed** /ɪmˈbærəst/ *adj* ashamed, nervous, or uncomfortable in a social situation: *I managed to spill water on one of the guests – I was so embarrassed!*| **[+ about]** *At about the age of twelve, girls start feeling embarrassed about changing their clothes in front of other people.*
>
> **ex·cit·ed** /ɪkˈsaɪtɪd/ *adj* happy, interested or hopeful because something good has happened or will happen: *Steve's flying home tomorrow – we're all very excited.* | *excited crowds of shoppers.* | **[+ about]** *The kids are so excited about Christmas.*
>
> **fright·ened** /ˈfraɪtnd/ *adj* feeling afraid: *a frightened animal*| **[+ of]** *I was frightened of being left by myself in the house.*
>
> **in·terest·ed** /ˈɪntrestɪd/ *adj* giving a lot of attention to something because you want to find out more about it: **[+ in]** *I'm not really interested in politics.*
>
> **sur·prised** /səˈpraɪzd/ *adj* having a feeling of surprise: *Mr Benson looked surprised when I told him I was leaving.* | **[+ at/by]** *We were all surprised at Sue's outburst.*
>
> **wor·ried** /ˈwʌrid/ *adj* unhappy because you keep thinking about a problem or are anxious about something: *Don't look so worried – we'll find him.*| **[about]** *She's so worried about her exams.*

1  bored __with__
2  confused _____
3  depressed _____
4  disappointed _____
5  embarrassed _____
6  excited _____
7  frightened _____
8  interested _____
9  surprised _____
10 worried _____

**b** Match a beginning from A with an ending from B. Then complete the sentences with a preposition.

**A**

1  [ *e* ]  Nobody seems to be interested
2  [  ]  I'm so bored
3  [  ]  Are you still frightened
4  [  ]  We were really disappointed
5  [  ]  Are you excited
6  [  ]  My boss was surprised
7  [  ]  Everyone seems to be worried
8  [  ]  Don't be embarrassed
9  [  ]  My sister's really depressed
10 [  ]  I'm not confused

**B**

a  _____ my decision to leave.
b  _____ saying what you really think.
c  _____ money at the moment.
d  _____ the dark?
e  __ *in* __ what I'm saying.
f  _____ my job.
g  _____ missing your party.
h  _____ her weight.
i  _____ English grammar any more.
j  _____ your wedding?

**5** Complete the following sentences so that they are true for you.

a  I'm always pleased when _____
_____ .

b  I'm a bit worried about _____
_____ at the moment.

c  I get very annoyed when _____
_____ .

d  When I feel depressed I usually _____
_____ .

e  I've never been frightened of _____
_____ .

f  I find _____
_____ really boring.

g  I've always been interested in _____
_____ .

## Passives

**6** Complete the gaps in these true news stories with the correct form of *be* or *have*.

a   A house in Brazil which ____*is*____ made of plastic bottles has won a prize.

b   Pizza-scented bathroom products _____ been created by an Italian cosmetics manufacturer.

c   Stars of the new extreme sport 'free running' will _____ shown on tv jumping between buildings and across rooftops.

d   A dog _____ been offered a gold credit card with a $10,000 limit.

e   A mother and daughter who hadn't seen each other for 17 years met when they _____ put in the same prison cell in Brazil.

f   A Mexican man who _____ shot  in the back and neck says his dog did it.

g   French bus drivers who _____ banned from wearing shorts and sunglasses in summer are going on strike.

h   An eight foot long dragon lizard who has a nerve disorder _____ being treated with Chinese acupuncture.

i   Five tourists were rescued by helicopter after they _____ been chased round a field by a bull for three hours.

j   A Romanian man's neighbours say they _____ being kept awake at night by the noise of his dog snoring.

**7** Look at the following sentences and write questions using the passive form.

a   George was taken to hospital because he had a heart attack. (ask why)
   *Why was George taken to hospital?*

b   The car was stolen between 10 p.m. and midnight. (ask when)

   _____ ?

c   Tickets for the concert are sold at all large music stores. (ask where)

   _____ ?

d   The new hospital will be built next to the old one. (ask where)

   _____ ?

e   The article was written by Urma Mackintyre. (ask who by)

   _____ ?

f   The open air concert has been cancelled. (ask why)

   _____ ?

g   Portuguese is spoken in Portugal and Brazil. (ask where)

   _____ ?

h   Napoleon was known as Boney. (ask what)

   _____ ?

i   The film was directed by Zeffirelli. (ask who by)

   _____ ?

j   Forty people have been injured. (ask how many)

   _____ ?

**8** Complete the sentences with the correct passive form of the verb in brackets.

a   In the UK, psychology ____*is taught*____ (teach) in universities but not usually in schools.

b   The body of a young man _____ (find) in the river yesterday.

c   Thirty-five cars _____ (steal) from the city centre since January.

d   Where _____ the next Olympics _____ (hold)?

e   Alcoholic drinks _____ (not sell) to children under the age of sixteen.

f   _____ the bridge _____ (build) a long time ago?

g   I'm sorry, but dinner _____ (not include) in the price of an overnight stay.

h   _____ the vegetables _____ (freeze) immediately after you pick them?

## Active or passive

**9** Read these texts and complete the gaps with the best form (active or passive) of the verbs in boxes below each text.

**A**

'... and this is the last stage of the production process. As you know, Swift trainers are very expensive, and the reason they (1) ____cost____ so much is that they (2) _____ of the highest quality leather. We (3) _____ over 10 million trainers to countries all round the world and our shoes (4) _____ by all types of people, from top athletes to children at school.'

| wear | make | cost | export |

**B**

'... and that (1) _____ a track from the latest CD by Didi Brown. The songs on the album (2) _____ by Didi herself when she (3) _____ in Ireland last year. The CD goes on sale next week and half the money from the sales (4) _____ to the 'Children In Need' fund.'

| write | give | stay | be |

**C**

This is the new Primera Consul, Sir. As you can see, it (1) _____ . The seats are more comfortable and there's a sunroof which (2) _____ when you press this button. This model also (3) _____ with all the latest safety features, which (4) _____ very carefully by our technicians before they leave the factory.

| come | open | check | redesign |

## Pronunciation
### Verbs often used in the passive

**10** a Complete the table with the past participles, according to their stress pattern.

| awarded | based | composed | created | directed |
| discovered | ~~invented~~ | manufactured | painted | |
| produced | released | translated | used | written |

| 1 ● | 2 ●• | 3 •● | 4 •●• | 5 ••●• |
|---|---|---|---|---|
| | | | invented | |

b **T6.2** Listen and check.

## Vocabulary
### Extreme adjectives

**11** a Complete the dialogues with an extreme adjective from page 65 of the Students' Book.

1 A: I bet Tessa was happy about her exam results.
  B: Oh yes, she was absolutely _delighted._

2 A: I'm not going in – the water's _____ !
  B: Oh come on, it's not that cold.

3 A: You're not frightened of spiders, are you?
  B: Oh yes I am – absolutely _____ , in fact.

4 A: Have you seen the _____ outfit that Roberta's wearing?
  B: Oh yes, she does look a bit silly, doesn't she?

5 A: I thought there were some really _____ moments in that film.
  B: Did you? I didn't think it was that funny.

6 A: And now to the sad news about Ernie Hope.
  B: Yes, his death will be a _____ loss for the entertainment industry.

7 A: I was _____ when Will told me about his divorce.
  B: I know, it was a surprise, wasn't it?

8 A: You look hot – do you want a cold drink?
  B: Yes, please, it's absolutely _____ outside.

b **T6.3** Listen and check.

## Vocabulary booster
### Entertainment

12 a Complete the table with the words in bold. (Some words can go in more than one category.)

'The first two or three **chapters** are a bit boring.'

'It has a really memorable **soundtrack**.'

'The **plot** is very difficult to follow.'

'The **lead singer** has a very unusual voice.'

'The **artwork** is very detailed.'

'I thought the **acting** was a bit wooden.'

'It's a **compilation** of modern jazz.'

'The orchestra will be playing **symphony** no. 2 in G major.'

'I'm waiting until it comes out in **paperback**.'

'This is the author's third **novel**, and by far her best.'

'There were some amazing **special effects**.'

'It's a modern day **version** of a classic.'

'The first two **tracks** are the best.'

'The **script** is really well written.'

'This is his first **album** for three years.'

'The **photography** is absolutely superb.'

| Movies | Music | Books |
|--------|-------|-------|
|        |       | chapters |
|        |       |       |
|        |       |       |
|        |       |       |
|        |       |       |

b Replace the words in bold with a word from part a.

1 My mother bought me a **collection** of 20th-century poetry. _compilation_

2 I don't like novels with a complicated **story**. _____

3 I'm looking for the **film music** of Love Story. _____

4 It sounds OK, but I prefer the original **way of playing it**. _____

5 This is a special edition of the CD with three bonus **pieces of music**.

_____

6 I was a bit disappointed by the **words of the film**. _____

7 What did you think of the **actors' performance**? _____

8 This is an early edition of the book, with the original **pictures**.

_____

## Listen and read
### Customer reviews

13 a **T6.4** Listen to and/ or read the customer reviews on the opposite page. Which person is reviewing:

1 a film? _____
2 a book? _____
3 a CD? _____

b Listen and/or read again. Are these statements true (T) or false (F)?

The reviewer of the Elvis Presley CD thinks that …

1 Presley's music is very popular at the moment. ___T___

2 *Bossa Nova Baby* has been remixed. _____

3 *Moody Blue* was a smash hit.

_____

The reviewer of *Terminator 3* thinks that …

4 it has more action than the previous two movies, although it is shorter. _____

5 the funny scene in the nightclub was a good idea.

_____

6 Linda Hamilton should have been in the movie. _____

The reviewer of the Harry Potter book …

7 used to think that Harry Potter books were only for children.

_____

8 doesn't understand why Harry Potter is angry a lot. _____

9 admires Rowling's ability to create sympathetic characters.

_____

10 thinks that the book is too long. _____

**Reviewer: George** from London

More of the King's top tunes and a follow-up to last year's smash hit album *Elvis Number Ones*, released at a time when the King's popularity is at an all time high. Two tracks stand out from the norm: a curious remix of *Rubberneckin'*, and an unreleased version of *I'm a Routabout*. Both songs are enjoyable to listen to, but not strong enough to be hits.

The rest of the album sounds like many an Elvis compilation of the last two and a half decades, with plenty of old classics and fans' favourites. Some of the highlights which non-fans as well as fans may enjoy are: *Loving You, I Need Your Love Tonight, Bossa Nova Baby* (potential remix material here?), *Always On My Mind* and *Moody Blue*. *Moody Blue* is a very good song, although recorded at a time when Elvis was not in great health. I believe this could have been a big smash hit for Elvis if it had come along in 1970–73 when he may have had more energy to put into the song, rather than 1976–77.

If you don't already have a lot of the songs on this CD then this is for you, especially as the technical sound quality of the songs will be better than on previous releases.

---

**Reviewer: Frankie** from Wales

This movie is far too short when you compare it to its predecessors, but in its 109 minutes you get more action than the first two movies combined, and you also get a great story.

The effects are second to none, which you expect with a Terminator movie and the pace starts at a blinding speed and never slows. There are some great moments of continuity from the first two movies and one or two cameos and returns of past characters. The movie is also not afraid to have its funny moments, such as Arnie walking into a nightclub naked on ladies night in search of clothing. The scene also gives some light relief from the movie's otherwise somewhat negative feel as humanity rolls closer to impending disaster.

While I may sound a little unpopular, I rate this instalment higher than its predecessors: the director does a better job than Cameron could ever hope to do. This is a fantastic chase movie, even more so than T2 ever was, and with T4 already written, I am eager to see what will happen next in the saga.

And no, I didn't miss Linda Hamilton as much as I thought I would: this movie has proved that it can do just as well, if not better without her presence.

---

**Reviewer: Jed Barker** from the USA

Until this summer, I have been guilty of writing off the Harry Potter books as 'mere children's books'. But after finally taking the time to read them, I realised what I have been missing all this time. Sure, they are kid-friendly, but they are witty, clever, and can be enjoyed by even a college student like myself. And I am very pleased to say that they get better and better with each instalment.

*Order of the Phoenix* takes a distinctly dark tone that was hinted at in *Goblet of Fire*. Harry is not a young kid any more, and yes, he is angry a lot, but with everything that he has had to deal with, he has every right to be. There is, of course, Voldemort on the loose and the Ministry of Magic trying to cover it up (a source of political satire in this novel). There is also a much-hyped 'death of a central character'. I won't reveal who the unfortunate person is, but I was quite upset when Rowling killed him/her off. That is yet another testament to her genius, the fact that she makes you care so much about her characters.

I thoroughly enjoyed this book. Anyone with a sense of fun and imagination should. It may not be a literary masterpiece, but it doesn't need to be. It's just fun. And yes, it's long, but it moves so fast that you can hardly believe that there are nearly 800 pages!

## Improve your writing
### Checking for mistakes

14 A student has written a customer review to post on the website on page 49. The teacher has used a correction code to help him find and correct his mistakes. Look at the code and then correct his mistakes.

∧  for a missing word
sp  for spelling
wo for word order
vf  for verb form
ww for a wrong word

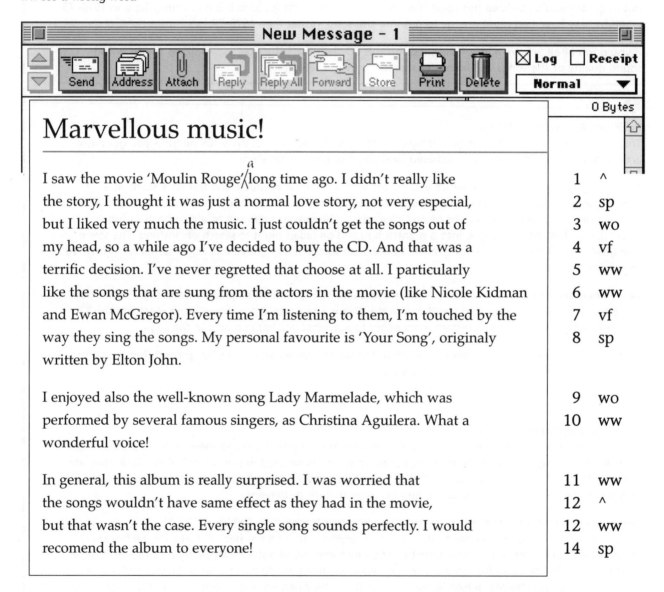

# Marvellous music!

|  |  |  |
|---|---|---|
| I saw the movie 'Moulin Rouge'ₐlong time ago. I didn't really like | 1 | ∧ |
| the story, I thought it was just a normal love story, not very especial, | 2 | sp |
| but I liked very much the music. I just couldn't get the songs out of | 3 | wo |
| my head, so a while ago I've decided to buy the CD. And that was a | 4 | vf |
| terrific decision. I've never regretted that choose at all. I particularly | 5 | ww |
| like the songs that are sung from the actors in the movie (like Nicole Kidman | 6 | ww |
| and Ewan McGregor). Every time I'm listening to them, I'm touched by the | 7 | vf |
| way they sing the songs. My personal favourite is 'Your Song', originaly | 8 | sp |
| written by Elton John. | | |
| | | |
| I enjoyed also the well-known song Lady Marmelade, which was | 9 | wo |
| performed by several famous singers, as Christina Aguilera. What a | 10 | ww |
| wonderful voice! | | |
| | | |
| In general, this album is really surprised. I was worried that | 11 | ww |
| the songs wouldn't have same effect as they had in the movie, | 12 | ∧ |
| but that wasn't the case. Every single song sounds perfectly. I would | 12 | ww |
| recomend the album to everyone! | 14 | sp |

# MODULE 7

## Vocabulary
### Going out

**1** Complete the reviews with words from Reading on pages 70 and 71 of the Students' Book.

---

### *CityLife*

#### The best pizzas: *Terracotta*

If you like Italian (a) <u>f o o d</u> at good prices, you will love this small (b) c _ _ _ _ of restaurants in west London. The food is simple and is made from high quality (c) i _ _ _ _ _ _ _ _ _ _. We visited the South Kensington restaurant and particularly liked the unusual home-made pasta dishes and the pizzas which are (d) b _ _ _ _ in traditional (e) o _ _ _ _ in full sight of the diners. The seating is comfortable and the service friendly.

**Terracotta is at South Kensington, Chelsea and Putney.
Tel: 0203 555 38712.**

*12 noon–2.30 p.m.*          *6 p.m.–midnight*

#### The best Latin American dancing: *Salsa Studio*

A favourite venue if you like this (f) d _ _ _ _ _ c _ _ _ _ from South America. This year Salsa Studio is celebrating five years in the business. Downstairs the well-loved (g) D_ , Nando de Novas mixes salsa, samba and Rio funk and keeps people dancing to the Brazilian beat until the early hours. Upstairs on Friday and Saturday nights there is a (h) l_ _ _ b _ _ _ , and this week sees the welcome return of popular group, Batmacumba.

**Salsa Studio: 424 High Street, Islington. 10 p.m.–3 a.m. €10.**

*Lessons also available: Beginners 7 p.m.–8 p.m., Intermediate 8 p.m.–9 p.m., Advanced 9 p.m.–10 p.m.*

#### The best (i) K _ _ _ _ _ _: *King Disco House*

Don't worry if you can't sing. We couldn't, but the friendly crowd at this bar in the centre of town still (j) a _ _ _ _ _ _ _ _ _ us! If you like to sing with a state-of-the-art sound system and colourful (k) l _ _ _ _ _ l _ _ _ _ _ , this is the place for you. The party-goers are a truly (l) i _ _ _ _ _ _ _ _ _ _ _ _ _ crowd: the night we went there were people from Japan, China, the UK, Germany, Spain and Russia. Highly recommended for a great night out!

**5 Lombard Street, W1.**

*Open 9.00 p.m.–1.00 a.m.*

---

## Vocabulary booster
### Food and cooking

**2** Circle the word which does not belong in each group.

a   cabbage   spinach   carrot   (peach)

b   plum   melon   cauliflower   pineapple

c   prawn   lamb   pork   beef

d   mayonnaise   garlic   soya sauce   ketchup

e   saucepan   spoon   mixing bowl   frying pan

f   boil   chop   roast   bake

g   tough   overdone   delicious   burnt

h   fork   corkscrew   tin opener   bottle opener

i   fresh   frozen   spicy   tinned

## Polite requests

**3** In the following dialogues is B saying 'yes, it's ok,' or 'no, it's not okay' to A's request? Circle Yes or No.

> A: Can I pay by visa?
> B: I'm afraid we only accept cash.

a   Yes/No

> A: Is it okay if I bring Susanna to the party?
> B: Sure, no problem. It'll be nice to see her.

b   Yes/No

> A: Do you mind if I phone you back later?
> B: I'll be out until three. Try after that.

c   Yes/No

> A: Could you possibly have a look at my computer?
> B: Of course.

d   Yes/No

> A: I'm going to be late home. Would you mind feeding the cat for me?
> B: Of course not.

e   Yes/No

> A: Do you mind waiting for a few minutes? The doctor's busy at the moment.
> B: Sorry, but I have to catch a train.

f   Yes/No

> A: Do you think you could come back later?
> B: Certainly.

g   Yes/No

**4** Put the words in the correct order to make polite requests.

a   me / you / Can / a / lend / pencil
*Can you lend me a pencil?* _____ ?

b   here / I / mind / if / you / sit / Do
_____ ?

c   speak / please / more / you / Could / slowly
_____ ?

d   bag / minute / you / after / mind / a / Would / for / looking / my
_____ ?

e   possibly / €20 / borrow / I / Could
_____ ?

f   mind / your / down / turning / Would / you / music
_____ ?

**5** **a** Correct the mistakes in the polite requests.

        *it*

1   A: Is/all right if I close the window?

    B: Yes, go ahead.

2   A: Would you helping me with my suitcase?

    B: I'm sorry but I've got a bad back.

3   A: Could I pass the salt, please?

    B: Yes, here you are.

4   A: Would you to bring us the bill, please?

    B: Certainly, Sir.

5   A: Do you mind I go now?

    B: No, that's fine. I think we've finished.

6   A: Do you mind getting me some milk?

    B: Of course not. How much do you need?

7   A: Could I possible have a look at your newspaper?

    B: Of course.

8   A: Would you mind to answer my phone while I'm out?

    B: I'm afraid I can't. I'm just going to a meeting.

**b** **T7.1** Listen and check. Then listen and repeat the dialogues, paying attention to sounding polite.

**6** a Look at the following situations and complete each question so that it is polite.

1 You want to pay by credit card.

Can _I pay by credit card_____ ?

2 You want to borrow your friend's camera.

Do you think _____ ?

3 You didn't hear what your classmate said. You want her to say it again.

Could _____ ?

4 You've written a letter in English. You want your teacher to check it.

Would you mind _____ ?

5 You can't hear what your flatmate is saying because of the radio. You want him to turn it down.

Would _____ ?

6 You need ten euros. You want your colleague to lend it to you.

Do you think _____ ?

7 You haven't finished your essay. You want to give it to your teacher a day late.

Do you mind if _____ ?

8 You need to use your colleague's computer.

Could I possibly _____ ?

9 Your friend asks you to go to the cinema with her. You can't tell her until tomorrow.

Is it okay _____ ?

b **T7.2** Listen to the situations and complete each question politely.

You hear:

You want to pay by credit card. Can ...

You say:

Can I pay by credit card?

# *will* for offers and instant decisions

**7** a Write full answers using *I'll* for offering and adding any necessary extra words.

1 A: I forgot to tell Jack about the meeting.
B: I / phone / him / you like
_I'll phone him if you like._

2 A: I'm really thirsty.
B: I / get / you / drink

_____

3 A: Hello, IT Support? My printer isn't working.
B: OK / I / come over / have / look

_____

4 A: I think I'm going to miss my train.
B: I / take you / station / you like

_____

5 A: This CD is great!
B: I / lend / it / you / you want

_____

6 A: Have you got the e-mail address for ACE?
B: No, but I / find / it and e-mail / it / you

_____

7 A: Can you give me some information about holidays in Greece?
B: Certainly. I / get you / brochure

_____

_____

8 A: This is a very interesting article.
B: I / photocopy it / you

_____

b **T7.3** Listen and check. Then listen and repeat the offers.

**8** Choose a sentence from each box to make a dialogue for the situations below.

**A**

> The black ones look really nice, Madam. ~~Are they comfortable?~~
> Could you possibly change my flight to the evening?
> Is there anything good on TV tonight?
> Hi! Nice to see you. Come in and have a coffee.
> Are you ready to order?
> Could I speak to Mrs Williams in the Accounts Department?
> I've got a problem with my shower. It isn't working.

**B**

> Okay, but I won't stay long, I can see you're busy.
> Yes, I'll have the fish.
> I'll just check the computer.
> Yes, very – I'll take them.
> I don't know – I'll have a look in the newspaper.
> I'll just see if she's available. Hold on please.
> I'll send someone up straightaway. Which room is it?

1  In a shoe shop

A: _The black ones look really nice, Madam._
   _Are they comfortable?_

B: _____

2  In a hotel

A: _____
   _____

B: _____
   _____

3  In a travel agent's

A: _____
   _____

B: _____

4  Visiting a friend's house

A: _____

B: _____
   _____

5  In a restaurant

A: _____

B: _____

6  Phoning someone's office

A: _____
   _____

B: _____

7  At home in the evening, relaxing

A: _____

B: _____
   _____

## will or going to

**9** Is the response instant or has the speaker already planned to do something? Complete the sentences with the correct form of *will* or *going to* and a verb from the box.

| ~~go~~ | go | see | spend | visit | walk |
|---|---|---|---|---|---|

1  A: It's Paul's birthday today.

   B: Is it? I _'ll go_ and get him a card.

2  A: Do you want to take a taxi home?

   B: No, I think I _____ . It's not far.

3  A: Would you like to go out for a meal tonight?

   B: Thanks, but I can't. Sue and I _____ the evening with my parents.

4  A: I've just seen Mark go into the café next door.

   B: Really? I haven't seen him for ages. I _____ in and say hello.

5  A: What are you doing this weekend?

   B: I _____ my brother and his girlfriend. They're having a barbecue.

6  A: What are you doing this weekend?

   B: I'm not sure. Maybe I _____ a film.

# Vocabulary
## Social behaviour

10 Use the clues to complete the crossword. All the words can be found in Vocabulary and speaking on page 74 of the Students' Book.

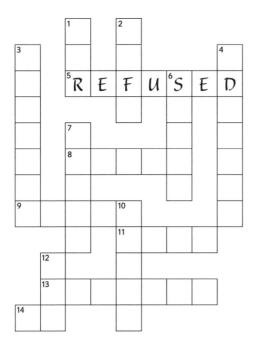

**Across**

5  Have you ever _____ food that someone has cooked for you?
8  Waiter: Are you ready to _____ , Madam?
9  People usually _____ up when they go to the opera. My mother always wears her best jewellery.
11 The show starts at seven so I'll _____ you up at six.
13 Have you been _____ to Jenny's birthday dinner?
14 'That was delicious. Can I wash _____ ?' 'No, sit down and relax.'

**Down**

1  I'll pay _____ the tickets.
2  Would you mind giving me a _____ home?
3  Carrie _____ to help Paolo cook dinner.
4  'Fifteen' is a very popular restaurant. You need to book two months in _____ .
6  'You're looking very _____ !' 'Yes, I'm taking Suzy to a posh restaurant.'
7  Yoko said goodbye and _____ to Mr Mori.
10 Let's _____ the bill. There are ten of us, so that's €15 each.
12 What about a _____ for the waiter? It's about 10% of the bill, isn't it?

# Pronunciation
## Lost letters

11 a In these words from module 7 one or more of the letters is not pronounced. Cross out the 'lost' letter(s). Say the words aloud to see what is missing and also use the phonemic script.

1  average
   /ˈævrɪdʒ/
2  restaurant
   /ˈrestrɒnt/
3  vegetable
   /ˈvedʒtəbəl/
4  international
   /ɪntəˈnæʃnəl/
5  different
   /ˈdɪfrənt/
6  traditional
   /trəˈdɪʃnəl/
7  business
   /ˈbɪznɪs/
8  favourite
   /ˈfeɪvrɪt/
9  several
   /ˈsevrəl/
10 fashionable
   /ˈfæʃnəbəl/

b ⬛T7.4 Listen and check. Then listen and repeat the words, paying attention to the stress.

## Listen and read
## Culture clash

**12** **a** You are going to listen to and/or read an article about problems that happen when people do business in other countries. Write down three things that you think could be a problem for British or American people doing business in your country. Think about such things as:

- [ ] dress
- [ ] time-keeping
- [ ] translation problems
- [ ] getting to know people personally
- [ ] advertising and marketing a product
- [ ] calling people by their first names
- [ ] business entertaining
- [ ] giving gifts

**b** **T7.5** Listen to and/or read the article. Put the items in part a in the order they are mentioned in the article. (Do not include the quiz questions.)

# CULTURE CLASH

In Africa a famous food company tried to sell its baby food by advertising it with the picture of a baby on the label. They did not know that this particular country used labels only to show a picture of the food inside! When Pepsico used the slogan 'Come Alive With Pepsi' in Taiwan, they had no idea that it would be translated into Chinese as 'Pepsi brings your ancestors back from the dead'.

Misunderstandings such as these about language or about culture are sometimes comical but can also cause genuine hurt or anger. Business styles and customs vary widely in different countries and what is normal in one culture can be completely unacceptable in another. How well is your company prepared? Try this short test. Look at the following situations. What mistakes have been made?

1 You are in Paris on business. In a meeting it is very hot and you suggest to everyone that they take off their ties and roll up their sleeves.

2 A Japanese businessman asks, 'When do you want the report?' 'Yesterday!' answers the American businesswoman.

3 In an Arabic country, a group from a British company are invited to a dinner party. They all bring gifts and during the evening they continue to talk about their work.

4 A sales manager in Hong Kong is angry because his workers are always fifteen minutes late for work. He makes a new rule that they all must come on time.

5 A Spanish secretary receives an urgent request to e-mail a report to the New York office before 2/3. She sends it on 1st March.

6 You are having a meal with Chinese colleagues in Nanjing. After the meal you use the hot towel to wipe your hands and your face.

How did you do? Did you spot the 'cultural clashes'? Well, in the first situation, French businessmen rarely take off their ties even if the weather is very hot. The idea of the American 'casual Friday' where the boss is called by his or her first name and people can wear jeans and trainers is a complete mystery to many other nationalities. In Germany for example, colleagues often call each other by their titles and surnames, (e.g. Herr Doktor) in the workplace.

For many western countries, 'time is money' and good business equals fast business. However, in some cultures people consider that building good relationships with business partners is more important. They think in months and years and not days and hours and find western executives impatient.

Socialising in different countries can be tricky. In Arabic countries, for example, people do not discuss business over meals. Giving gifts is another potential problem: in the UK most people take presents to a dinner party, but in many countries this is not polite because it suggests you think the host is poor.

The Hong Kong story is true. The workers started coming on time but they also stopped exactly on time instead of working into the night as they used to do and left a great deal of work unfinished.

The Spanish secretary was a month late. She didn't realise that in America the month is written before the day whereas in Europe the day comes first.

Finally, in the Chinese restaurant it is bad manners to wipe your face with a towel. Chinese people use it only for their hands.

So how did you do? Are you culturally aware or do you need a course in cross-cultural relationships? Whatever you do, remember that your way is not the only way and it is important to respect other people's customs.

## Making generalisations

**13** Use the prompts to make sentences about the advice in the Culture Clash article in exercise 11.

a French businessmen / tend / keep their ties on.
   *French businessmen tend to keep their ties on.*

b In the USA / perfectly normal / people / wear casual clothes on Fridays.
   _____ .

c Germans / tend not / call colleagues by their first names.
   _____ .

d In Japan / more important / build relationships than / finish business quickly.
   _____
   _____ .

e In many Arabic countries / not acceptable / talk about business during meals.
   _____
   _____ .

f In the UK / important / take a gift to a dinner party.
   _____ .

g In Spain / normal / write 2nd July as 2/7.
   _____ .

h In China / not usual / use a hot towel to wipe your face.
   _____ .

## Wordspot
### *go*

**14** a Complete the chant with the phrases in the box. Use the Present simple form in the first verse and the Past simple form in the second verse.

| go swimming    go out    go to bed    go for |
| go away    go for a coffee    ~~go out~~ |

On Mondays I always **(1)** _go out_ for a drink
And have a good long chat.
On Tuesdays I often **(2)** _____ a walk
Then **(3)** _____ at my best friend's flat.
On Wednesdays and Thursdays I stay at home
And **(4)** _____ at eight.
On Fridays I sometimes **(5)** _____ for a meal
And get back really late!
I **(6)** _____ for most weekends
To the beach and my house by the sea.
I **(7)** _____ and shopping on Saturdays
And on Sundays I'm home by three.

On Monday John **(8)** _went out_ for a drink
And had a good long chat.
On Tuesday night he **(9)** _____ a walk
Then **(10)** _____ at his best friend's flat.
On Wednesday and Thursday he stayed at home
And **(11)** _____ at eight.
On Friday night he **(12)** _____ for a meal
And got back really late.
He **(13)** _____ for the whole weekend
To the beach and his house by the sea.
He **(14)** _____ late on Saturday
And was dead by half past three!

b **T7.6** Listen to the chant and try to say it with the recording.

## Improve your writing
## Sending and replying to invitations by e-mail

15 a Read these e-mails and match the three invitations with their replies.

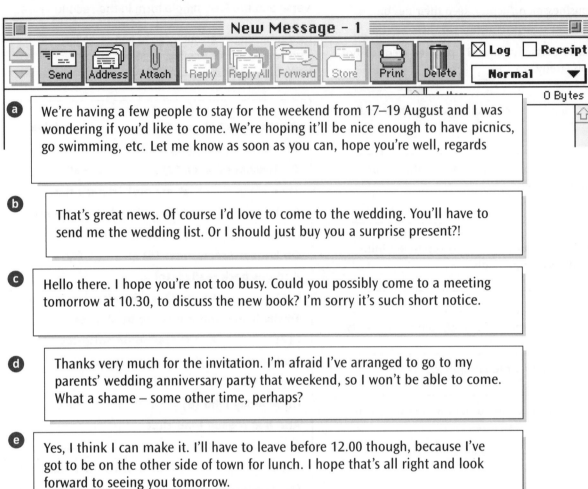

**New Message – 1**

Send  Address  Attach  Reply  Reply All  Forward  Store  Print  Delete

☒ Log  ☐ Receipt

Normal ▼

0 Bytes

**a** We're having a few people to stay for the weekend from 17–19 August and I was wondering if you'd like to come. We're hoping it'll be nice enough to have picnics, go swimming, etc. Let me know as soon as you can, hope you're well, regards

**b** That's great news. Of course I'd love to come to the wedding. You'll have to send me the wedding list. Or I should just buy you a surprise present?!

**c** Hello there. I hope you're not too busy. Could you possibly come to a meeting tomorrow at 10.30, to discuss the new book? I'm sorry it's such short notice.

**d** Thanks very much for the invitation. I'm afraid I've arranged to go to my parents' wedding anniversary party that weekend, so I won't be able to come. What a shame – some other time, perhaps?

**e** Yes, I think I can make it. I'll have to leave before 12.00 though, because I've got to be on the other side of town for lunch. I hope that's all right and look forward to seeing you tomorrow.

**f** I know it's a strange time to be sending e-mail, but I can't sleep! Jon and I have decided to get married and I wanted you to be the first person I invited to the wedding. It's going to be in Dublin on Saturday September 9th. I'll send you a proper invitation in the post – but I do hope you can come. If you're still awake, please reply!

1 an invitation to a meeting _____ , reply _____

2 a wedding invitation _____ , reply _____

3 an invitation to stay for the weekend _____ , reply _____

b Look at the e-mails again and underline useful phrases for inviting and for accepting or refusing an invitation.

c Write an invitation (using e-mail if you have it at home/work/school) and show it to your teacher.

## Vocabulary
## Technology

**1** Use the clues to complete the grid. All the words can be found in Reading on pages 80 and 81 of the Students' Book.

|   | a | | | | | | |
|---|---|---|---|---|---|---|---|
|   | S | O | F | T | W | A | R | E |

Grid letters (vertical spine): S O F T W A R E / E / C / H / N / O / L / O / G / I / C / A / L

a The problem seems to be with the s_oftware_ and not the computer itself.

b If you are still experiencing problems, please phone our h_____ d_____ on 0254 7395.

c Greg used to work at a c_____-c_____ , but it was very stressful because all the people phoning were frustrated and angry.

d My t_____ really hurts because I've been doing so much texting.

e The combined DVD/video player comes with a complete instruction m_____ .

f The information in last year's guidebook is already o_____ o_____ d_____ .

g The receptionist put me o_____ h_____ for ten minutes and then told me to call back!

h I take my l_____ on the train with me so that I can answer all my e-mails before I arrive at the office.

i How many text m_____ can your mobile store?

j If you've got a d_____ camera, you can e-mail me a photo.

k I'm going to phone the customer c_____ department and ask them how to reset my palmtop.

l We will have to contact BMW in Germany for the necessary s_____ p_____ for your car.

m You get a better picture q_____ with LCD TV screens.

## Defining relative clauses

**2** **a** Match the sentence beginnings in A with the endings in B. All the information comes from Modules 1–7. Then complete the gaps with *who*, *which*, *whose* or *where*.

**A**
1 [c] A leisure time activity is something
2 [ ] A determined person is someone
3 [ ] The Jim twins were brothers
4 [ ] An archaeological site is a place
5 [ ] A brilliant film is one
6 [ ] A confident person is someone
7 [ ] Kobe is the town in Japan
8 [ ] A disappointing book is one

**B**

a _____ people have found important historical buildings or objects.

b _____ believes in their own ability to do something.

c ___ *which* ___ you enjoy doing in your free time.

d _____ Karaoke probably started.

e _____ knows what they want and works hard to get it.

f _____ we expect to be better than it is.

g _____ lives were remarkably similar.

h _____ people think is very good.

**b** **T8.1** Listen and check.

3 Pete is talking to Les about his holiday plans. Look at the relative pronouns in bold and bracket the ones which can be omitted.

PETE: We're thinking of going to Spain this year. You went there last year, didn't you?

LES: Yes, that's right. Actually I've got some photos (**which**) I can show you of where we went. It was Mohacar on the south coast. A friend **whose** daughter went there last year recommended it.

PETE: Oh, someone **who** I work with has been to Mohacar. It's a very quiet area, isn't it?

LES: Yes, the thing **that** I liked most about it was the relaxing atmosphere. It's a place **where** you can forget all your problems.

PETE: How do you get there?

LES: Well you can fly to Almeria, but that's quite expensive, or you can take any flight **which** goes to Malagar and drive east along the coast. I know several people **who** have done that. Anyway, do you want to see the photos?

4 a Here are the photos from Les's holiday last year. Les is talking about the photos. Join his two sentences to make one, using a relative pronoun.

a This is the apartment. We rented it …

*This is the apartment which / that we rented*

b … and these are the people. They were staying in the apartment next door.

*and these are the people who were staying in the apartment next door.*

a This is the balcony. We had breakfast there every morning …

_____

_____

b … and this is the beach. It was right in front of our apartment.

_____

_____

a This is a bar. It stayed open till three in the morning …

_____

_____

b … and this is the man. He owned it.

_____

_____

a   This is a fish restaurant. We had excellent meals there …

_____

_____

b   … and this is a local woman. I can't remember her name.

_____

_____

a   This is one day. We went on a boat trip …

_____

_____

b   … and these are the men. We borrowed their boat

_____

_____

a   This is a market. It was open every Wednesday …

_____

_____

b   … and this is me wearing a hat. I bought it there.

_____

_____

b   Look again at the sentences you have made and bracket the relative pronoun if it can be omitted.

## Vocabulary
## People, places, jobs, everyday objects, machines and technology

5   Complete the table with the words in the box.

| alarm clock    bodyguard    call centre |
| computer nerd    cook    cooker |
| customer care department    kettle    dishwasher |
| help desk    laptop    launderette    make-up    palm |
| pilot    palm top    pencil sharpener    plumber |
| saucepan    stationers    techie    technophobe |
| voice mail |

| people | |
| places | |
| jobs | |
| everyday objects | |
| machines and technology | |

## Vocabulary
### How machines work

**6** a Complete these conversations to Helpdesks using vocabulary from page 83 of the Students' Book.

**1**

A: Good morning, Patricia speaking. How can I help?

B: Hello. I've got a problem with my PC. I was working on a document this morning and the computer (a) _crashed_ three times.

A: Okay, can I just check. Did you (b) s_____ it d_____ properly last night?

B: Mmm. Maybe not. It was on this morning.

A: OK, well I think the best thing to do now is to (c) r_____ it and see if that works.

**2**

A: Good morning, Meccaphone, George speaking.

B: Hi! I hope you can help. My mobile's gone dead.

A: How long have you had it?

B: A week.

A: It probably needs (a) r_____ .

B: And another thing ... I can't hear the ringing tone very well.

A: That's easy to fix. You just need to (b) t_____ u_____ the volume. What you have to do is ...

**3**

A: Hello, Meccaphone, George speaking.

B: Hi. I'm having problems with my (a) a_____ m_____ . Three people have told me that they left a (b) m_____ on it but I can't hear anything when I try to (c) r_____ them.

A: Does it use a cassette?

B: Yes.

A: Well, I think you may need to (d) r_____ the cassette. It sounds as if it is full.

B: I've tried that.

A: OK. Well I suggest that first of all you (e) s_____ o_____ the machine and then (f) s_____ it o_____ again.

B: OK. I've done that.

A: Can you see a red (g) b_____ at the back?

B: Yes.

A: ... well, (h) p_____ that and it will clear the display and you can start again.

b  **T8.2**  Listen and check.

## Quantifiers

**7** a Are the words in the box countable or uncountable? If they are countable, are they singular or plural? Write them in the correct category.

| banana | chair | children | fruit | information |
|---|---|---|---|---|
| jewellery | milk | money | news | people | person |
| petrol | pollution | potatoes | price | rice | ring |
| storm | sugar | traffic | vegetable | weather |

**Countable singular**
*banana*

**Countable plural**

**Uncountable**

b Underline the correct form of the verb *be*.

1 The children *is* / *are* upstairs.

2 The fruit *isn't* / *aren't* ready to eat yet.

3 The weather *was* / *were* very bad.

4 Who *is* / *are* the people behind you in the photo?

5 Petrol *is* / *are* getting more and more expensive.

6 How much money *is* / *are* there in my bank account?

7 *Is* / *Are* the jewellery real?

8 The traffic *was* / *were* terrible.

9 I'm afraid there *is* / *are* no news yet.

10 The information you were given *was* / *were* wrong.

11 Pollution *is* / *are* getting worse each year.

**8** **a** Sandra is trying to persuade Aileen to go to a party but Aileen doesn't want to go. Match Aileen's comments with a response from Sandra. Then complete the gaps with the words in the box.

| anything | couple | enough | few | got | have | lots of |
|----------|--------|--------|-----|-----|------|---------|
| many | much | no | isn't | of | plenty | some |

(anything and some are crossed out)

**Aileen:**

1 [ e ]
I haven't got *anything* to wear.

2 [ ]
I've got _____ friends.

3 [ ]
I haven't _____ much money.

4 [ ]
There'll be too _____ people.

5 [ ]
I never _____ anything to say.

6 [ ]
I've got too _____ homework to do.

7 [ ]
There _____ enough time to get ready.

**Sandra:**

a
You've got a _____ of hours tomorrow when you could finish it.

b
There's _____ time – we don't need to be there until nine!

c
Don't be silly. You've got _____ you could talk about.

d
Come on ... you've got loads _____ friends.

e
But you've got _some_ really nice clothes.

f
You only need _____ for a taxi.

g
Oh, but only a _____ people are coming.

**b** `T8.3` Listen and check.

**9** Correct the mistake in each sentence.

a Now my father is retired he's got plenty ⁄of time for his hobby: surfing the Internet.

b I think the soup needs a few salt. It doesn't have much taste.

c There were too many people and too many noise, so Jan couldn't see or hear the Prime Minister.

d I don't think there's enough of food for 100 people.

e Lisbon has got loads of good shops but there's not much of parking space in the city centre.

f There are plenty of tickets left for the afternoon performance, but no many for the evening.

g I want to thank everyone who has given me a lot support.

h There's plenty things to eat, so please help yourself.

i We've got lot of friends who live nearby.

j We haven't got some milk in the fridge.

k There were loads things to do before the party started; fortunately David helped.

l Sorry, but I can't go on holiday with you. I've got none money.

## 10 Complete these sentences so that they are true for you.

a   I've got too many _____ .

b   There are a lot of _____ in my bedroom.

c   I haven't got enough _____ .

d   I don't drink much _____ .

e   I eat plenty of _____ .

f   I don't know any _____ .

g   I read loads of _____ .

# Vocabulary
## Describing everyday objects

## 11 Each of these two items often have something in common. What is it? Think about the material, the shape, the size, what they are used for, etc. Use words and expressions from page 85 of the Students' Book

a   shoes and handbags
   _They're both made of leather._

b   a window and a wine bottle
   _____

c   a knife and scissors
   _____

d   a camera and a torch
   _____

e   sellotape and glue
   _____

f   a briefcase and a basket
   _____

g   a diamond ring and a painting by Picasso
   _____

h   a jumper and a scarf
   _____

i   a glass ornament and a vase
   _____

# Listen and read
## eBay

## 12 a  T8.4  Listen and/or read the text about eBay. Choose the best answers to the questions.

1   eBay is …
   a   a shop     b   a website     c   an office

2   The writer … things on eBay.
   a   bought     b   found     c   sold

3   You can buy and sell … things on eBay
   a   lots of different     b   unusual     c   expensive

4   People … can use eBay.
   a   in Europe     b   in the USA     c   all over the world

b   Listen and/or read again and answer the questions.

1   You want to sell something on eBay. What three things do you have to do?

   _____

   _____

2   You want to buy the following things. Which category would you look in?

   a   a ticket for the 2002 Football World Cup final

   _____

   b   a motorcycle

   _____

   c   an apartment in Chicago

   _____

   d   a pretty ornament of a cat

   _____

3   How did people find out about the company before 1996? _____

4   When did a lot of Internet companies have problems? _____

5   Has eBay ever had any serious problems?

   _____

6   Who is the Chief Executive Officer of eBay?

   _____

7   How does eBay make a profit?

   _____

8   Did the writer manage to sell everthing?

   _____

Yesterday I cleared up my house and I mean really cleared up my house. The room that gave the most results was my husband's 'office.' There I found: one right-footed walking boot, size 10 (he lost the other one somewhere), a garden badminton set, complete with rackets and a net (we decided to get fit last summer and played with it once), a set of Star Wars videos and two small china cats someone gave me last birthday. I collected these and other 'finds', took them downstairs and logged on to www.eBay.com: the answer to all our rubbish – or 'one person's junk is another person's treasure.'

What is eBay? The simple answer is that it is the world's most popular auction house. The website says, 'eBay's mission is to provide a global trading platform where practically anyone can trade practically anything,' – yes, even one right-footed boot. People can sell and buy in a range of over 300 categories, including cars and other vehicles, movies and DVDs, sporting goods, collectibles, travel, tickets, musical instruments, real estate, clothes and shoes, jewellery – the list goes on and on.

The idea came from Peter Omidyar. Born in Paris, Omidyar, moved to Washington when he was still a child. At High School he became very interested in computer programming and after graduating from Tuft University in 1988, he worked for the next few years as a computer engineer. In his free time he started eBay as a kind of hobby, originally offering the service free by word of mouth. By 1996 there was so much traffic on the site that he had to upgrade and he began charging a fee to members. Joined by a friend, Peter Skoll, and in 1998 by his dynamic CEO, Meg Whitman, he has never looked back. Even in the great dot com crashes of the late 1990s eBay went from strength to strength. It is now one of the ten most visited online shopping sites on the Internet.

If you think about it, it's a perfect Internet idea. It sells connections not goods, putting buyer and seller into contact with each other. All you have to do is take an e-photo, write a description, fill out a sales form and you're in business; the world is your market place. Oh, and of course for each item sold eBay gets a percentage and that is a great deal of money: Everyday there are more than sixteen million items listed on eBay and eighty percent of items are sold.

Some of the more bizarre items up for offer have been a piece of French toast, partially eaten by Justin Timberlake, advertising space on a man's head, a pair of used false teeth, and 'Nothing' (the seller said he would give the profits to a local university).

One week later I am the proud possessor of a clean and tidy home and €110 in cash. Someone even bought the boot.

# Pronunciation
## /ʒ/, /ʃ/, /dʒ/ and /tʃ/

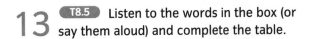

Compare these sounds:
television  **sho**p  **j**ourney  tea**ch**er
/ʒ/        /ʃ/     /dʒ/           /tʃ/

**13** **T8.5** Listen to the words in the box (or say them aloud) and complete the table.

| anti-social | channel | digital | feature | instruction |
| machine | manufactured | tissues | messaging |
| passion | picture | switch | possession | re-charge |
| revision | sharp | stationers | technology |
| television | washing machine | old-fashioned |

| /ʒ/ | /ʃ/ | /dʒ/ | /tʃ/ |
|---|---|---|---|
| | anti-social | | |
| | | | |
| | | | |
| | | | |

b  Listen again and repeat the words.

# Improve your writing
## Formal and informal styles

**14** a  Look at the two letters about things which have been lost. The first is informal and the second is more formal. Complete the gaps with the phrases.

I don't suppose you've found it / I do hope it has been found

could you post it / I would be grateful if you could send it

let me know how much the postage is / I will of course pay for postage

I am writing to enquire whether / ~~Just writing to say~~

---

46 Broom Way
23rd February

Dear Andy,

(1) __Just writing to say__ thanks again for having us last weekend. We both had a really good time.

The only thing is, I've lost one of my earrings: I know I was wearing it on Sunday and when we got home, I couldn't find it. Perhaps it fell off while I was playing with the children in the garden.
(2) _____?

I don't know if you remember it. It's quite big, made of silver, with a blue stone set in it. The earrings are quite special to me because they were a birthday present from Peter.

If you do happen to find it, (3) _____
to me? Obviously, (4) _____ .
Anyway, I'll keep my fingers crossed!

Lots of love,
Ingrid

---

22 Prince Avenue,
Horbury

The Manager,
Sherbon Hotel,
Vermont

27th March

Dear Sir/Madam,

(5) _____ you have found a camera which I left in my hotel room last weekend. I was staying in room 201 from 21st–23rd. I am almost certain that I left the camera in the bedside cabinet.

(6) _____ since it is a very expensive model. It is a Nikon compact, in a black leather case with a red and black strap.

(7) _____ by registered post to the above address. (8) _____ .

Yours faithfully,

Ian Crompton

b  Imagine that you have just finished a language course in the UK, and you realise that you have left something in a classroom. Write to the school to ask about it. The address is: Success Language School, Dewbury Road, Brighton.

## Vocabulary
### Prepositions

**1** Complete the sentences with a word from each box. The phrases all come from Reading and vocabulary on pages 92 of the Students' book.

| amounted | ~~glued~~ | idea | launched | linked |
|---|---|---|---|---|
| turned | value | way | | |

| down | from | of | of | on | ~~to~~ | to | to |
|---|---|---|---|---|---|---|---|

a During the first moon landing in 1969, millions of people were _____glued to_____ their televisions.

b In the nineteenth century most people thought the _____ flight was nonsense.

c None of Schiller's early experiments before he was thirty. _____ anything.

d By the end of the 1970s vinyl records were _____ their _____ out.

e Several publishers _____ his book before it was eventually accepted.

f My computer is _____ the network via a modem.

g The discovery of penicillin was _____ enormous _____ in the Second World War.

h The satellite was _____ Cape Canaveral.

## Making predictions with *will/won't*

**2** Put *will ('ll)* or *won't* in the best place in the sentences.

a Don't worry. I/forget!  *won't*

b Why don't you buy Meg this bag? She love it!

c I know I win but I buy a lottery ticket every week.

d Let me make a photocopy. It take long.

e There be lots of food at the party.

f The flight takes hours so you arrive at ten o'clock.

g Don't panic. The coach go without you!

h I'm going to the conference in Lisbon. You be there?

## *likely to*

**3** Complete the sentences with *is/are/isn't/aren't likely to* and the verb in brackets.

a You _'re likely to find_ (find) the food strange at first.

b The weather _____ (get) worse, so bring an umbrella.

c Rooney _____ (not play) on Saturday.

d The news _____ (be) bad. They think a lot of people were hurt.

e You _____ (not improve) if you don't practise.

f We _____ (sleep) much tonight. They're having a party next door.

g Passengers _____ (experience) long delays at the airport.

## *may well*

**4 a** Complete the answers using *may well* and a verb from the box.

| cancel | fail | ~~find~~ | get married | leave | snow |
|---|---|---|---|---|---|

1 A: I've never done any Salsa dancing before.
  B: In that case, you __may well find__ it best to take some lessons.

2 A: Melanie seems unhappy in her job.
  B: Yes. She _____ the company soon.

3 A: How long have Jon and Sylvie been going out with each other?
  B: Almost a year now and they _____ next year.

4 A: I am phoning to check my flight. It's BA 2517.
  B: Conditions are very poor at the moment and they _____ the flight.

5 A: When is your driving test?
  B: In two days' time. I feel okay about the practical but I _____ the written exam.

6 A: It's very cold, isn't it? Have you seen the weather forecast today?
  B: Yes. It _____ later.

b **T9.1** Listen and check.

## Different ways of making predictions

5 Reorder the words in these sentences. The first word is underlined.

a  tonight / see / I'll / definitely / Ray
   *I'll definitely see Ray tonight.*

b  probably / pass / Carlos / his / exam / won't
   _____
   _____

c  stay / New York / decide / in / Teresa / may / to
   _____
   _____

d  get / isn't / to / Sandy / job / likely / the
   _____
   _____

e  next / almost / I'll / computing / year / do / certainly / a / course
   _____
   _____

f  so / could / us / late / don't / We / for / wait / be
   _____
   _____

g  weekend / away / probably / We / this / go / won't
   _____
   _____

h  loads / are / on / There / the / likely / beach / be /. to / people / of
   _____
   _____

6 a  Rewrite these sentences so that they mean the same, using the words in brackets.

1  Brazil are likely to win the World Cup.
   Brazil __may well win the__ World Cup. (may well)

2  I'm sure we won't have time to do any sightseeing.
   We _____
   _____ . (definitely)

3  It'll probably rain before the end of the day.
   It _____
   _____ . (likely)

4  Perhaps my friend Mari will be a famous actress one day.
   My friend Mari _____
   _____ . (could)

5  My boss is very unlikely to agree to the pay rise.
   My boss _____
   _____ . (almost certainly)

6  I think you'll recognise my sister when you see her.
   You _____
   _____ . (probably)

7  We probably won't get back from the theatre before midnight.
   We _____
   _____ . (likely)

8  I'm sure that our teacher will give us a lot of homework for the weekend.
   Our teacher _____
   _____ . (almost certainly)

b  **T9.2** Listen to the sentences and change them, using the prompts given.

You hear:                    You say:

Brazil are likely to win the World Cup. (may well)

Brazil may well win the World Cup.

## Vocabulary
## Society and change

7 a Write ↑ or ↓.

1 become more (+ adjective) ↑
2 decrease ＿＿＿
3 go up ＿＿＿
4 get better ＿＿＿
5 fall ＿＿＿
6 become less (+ adjective) ＿＿＿
7 increase ＿＿＿
8 deteriorate ＿＿＿
9 get worse ＿＿＿
10 go down ＿＿＿
11 improve ＿＿＿
12 rise ＿＿＿

b Complete the newspaper articles using different phrases from part a. (More than one phrase is possible in each case.)

## UK divorce rate improves

The number of people who get divorced has (1) _decreased / fallen / gone down_ to a ten-year low according to the Office for National Statistics. There were 144,600 divorces last year compared with 158,000 ten years ago. It is the third year that the number of divorces has (2) ＿＿＿＿＿＿＿＿ .

Unfortunately, however, getting divorced is becoming a habit. The number of people divorcing for the second or third time has (3) ＿＿＿＿＿＿＿＿ sharply. It is now almost double the number of ten years ago.

## Equality at work?

The number of working women has (4) ＿＿＿＿＿＿＿＿ dramatically in the last fifty years. In 1960 one in four married women went out to work. Today, nearly three out of four do so.

However, most employees in the lowest-paid professions are women. Their conditions of work have not (5) ＿＿＿＿＿＿＿＿ much, and it is normal to work long hours for minimum pay. In some cases, in fact, the conditions have (6) ＿＿＿＿＿＿＿＿ since the 1960s, with employers demanding longer hours at difficult times. To balance this, it has (7) ＿＿＿＿＿＿＿＿ easier for women to climb to the top of their profession and the number of female managers, directors, top lawyers and doctors is significantly greater.

## Geniuses should not get married

Geniuses should not get married, according to Dr Satoshi Kanazawa of New Zealand. Male scientists tend to have their biggest successes before their mid-thirties and after that their ability to invent or discover something important rapidly (8) ＿＿＿＿＿＿＿＿ . Just like male birds and animals, young men are competitive and want to attract females; their creativity (9) ＿＿＿＿＿＿＿＿ during their twenties and thirties, but as soon as they get married and have families, it begins to disappear.

## Hypothetical possibilities with *if*

**8** **a** Complete the questions about imaginary situations with the correct form of the verbs in brackets.

1  If you ___won___ a lot of money, what ___would___ you ___do___ with it? (win, do)

2  What _____ you _____ if someone _____ to rob you in the street? (do, try)

3  If you _____ on the motorway, _____ you _____ of the car ? (break down, get out)

4  _____ you _____ what to do if someone _____ their arm badly? (know, cut)

5  If you _____ a friend of yours was stealing money from his company, _____ you _____ anyone? (know, tell)

6  _____ you _____ safe walking home alone at night in your town? (feel)

7  If someone _____ you a free bungee jump, what _____ you _____? (offer, do)

8  _____ you ever _____ raw meat? (eat)

**b**  Match these answers to the questions above.

a  ☐  If I was hungry enough, yes, I would.

b  ☐  I think I'd probably tie something round it.

c  ☐  No, I wouldn't. I'd lock the doors and stay inside.

d  ☐  I might do it for the experience if I was feeling brave!

e  ☐  I might tell another friend so that we could decide what to do.

f  ☐  I'd probably just give him all my money and run.

g  ☐  No, I definitely wouldn't. It's too dangerous after dark here.

h  ☐1  I'd travel round the world.

**c**  What would you do in the situations in part a. Write your answers using *I'd, I wouldn't, I might, I could.*

1  _____

2  _____

3  _____

4  _____

5  _____

6  _____

7  _____

8  _____

## Real and hypothetical possibilities with *if*

**9** **a** Complete the gaps in these conversations with the best form of the verb in brackets.

**❶**  CLARE'S GOING TO HAVE A BABY. SHE'S TALKING TO HER FRIEND JACKIE ABOUT IT.

CLARE:  I can't decide whether to have the baby in hospital or not.

JACKIE:  Well, I (a) _'d go_ (go) into hospital, especially as it's your first baby.

CLARE:  Yes, you're probably right.

JACKIE:  Have you decided on a name yet?

CLARE:  Yes – if it (b) _____ (be) a boy, we (c) _____ (call) him Tom, and if it (d) _____ (be) a girl, Sara.

**❷**  TIM'S MOTHER IS VERY WORRIED BECAUSE SHE'S HAD A LETTER FROM HIS SCHOOL, SAYING THAT HE HAS MISSED A LOT OF LESSONS.

MOTHER:  Why aren't you going to your classes?

TIM:  Because they're so boring: I (a) _____ (go) if they (b) _____ (be) more interesting. And I always get bad marks.

MOTHER:  Well, that's not surprising: if you (c) _____ (spend) less time playing computer games and (d) _____ (work) harder, you (e) _____ (not have) so many problems.

**b**  **T9.3**  Listen and check.

## *If* sentences in social situations

We often use *if* sentences in the following ways:
- Asking for permission:
  ***Would** you mind if I **opened** the window?*
  ***Would** you mind if I **left** early today?*
- Giving advice:
  *If I **were** you, I'd go home.*
  *You'll feel much better if you **have** a rest.*
- Making offers:
  *I'll phone her if you **like**.*
  *I'll fetch your car if you **give** me the keys.*
- Accepting invitations:
  *Thank you, that **would** be very nice.*

**10 a** Use the prompts to write complete sentences or questions for these situations.

1 Your friend has a letter to post. You are going out and offer to post it. What do you say?
I / post it / if / want
*I'll post it if you want.*

2 It's your first evening with a host family in England and you want to telephone home. How do you ask your landlady?
all right / if / I / use / phone?
_____ ?

3 Your friend is expecting a call from John, but she has to go out. What do you say?
I / take / message / if / he / phone
_____ .

4 You're on a crowded train and you want to open a window. How do you ask the other passengers?
anyone mind / if / I / open a window?
_____ ?

5 Your car's broken down and a friend offers to take you home. What does he say?
I / give / you / lift / if / like
_____ .

6 A friend invites you to eat in a new restaurant. What do you say?
That / be / great!
_____ !

7 It's snowing heavily and your friend wants to drive home. How do you advise her?
I / not / drive in this weather / if / I / be / you
_____
_____ .

**b** **T9.4** Listen to the situations and respond, using the prompts.

You hear:
Your friend has a letter to post. You are going out and offer to post it. I'll …

You say:
*I'll post it if you want.*

## Wordspot
*make*

**11** Complete the sentences with the correct form of *make* and the phrases in the box.

| of leather | a decision | a drink | a mistake |
| a noise | a ~~suggestion~~ | an appointment | sure |

a Can I __*make a suggestion*__ ? Why don't we have lunch now and discuss this later?

b I'm sorry, I think I've _____ . The answer should be 40,000 not 4,000!

c I'll _____ everyone _____ . What would you like, coffee or tea?

d Our company's handbags used to be _____ but nowadays we use some plastic as well.

e Before you go on a long car journey you need to _____ you check the oil level.

f The computer is _____ terrible _____ . What should I do?

g Doctor Maynard is free at four o'clock. Would you like to _____ ?

h It has taken a long time to _____ but we have decided to go to New York for our holiday.

71

## Listen and read
### Stuck on a desert island?

12 **a** If you were stuck on a desert island, what three things would you miss most and what three things would you miss least about your life?

most _____
_____

least _____
_____
_____

**b** T9.5 Listen to and/or read the discussion on a website. Did any of the people choose the same things as you?

**c** Who ...

1 would be lonely?
2 would not enjoy the silence?
3 would miss food or drink?
4 would hate being on a desert island?

**d** Are these statements true (T) or false (F)?

1 Steve would be bored by too much sunny weather.
2 Tomas would probably hate being alone.
3 Nobody would miss living in a city.
4 Paola hates getting letters.
5 Three people would miss technology.
6 Jaime enjoys school.

# TALKINGPOINTS.com

## Stuck on a desert island?

Started on 23rd August by Steve B          Posts 1–7 of 42

**Post 1          Steve, USA**

Hi everyone,
What would you miss most and least if you were stuck on a desert island? For me it would be the changing seasons, especially the fall in New England. Sure, it would be fantastic to have non-stop sun, but I'd miss the colours of the seasons. I guess this will sound stupid but I'd probably miss the rain too! I wouldn't miss getting up at six every day to go to work, though! What about you?

**Post 2          Tomas, Germany**

Good question, Steve. I think I'd miss the pastries and different types of bread, and shopping at the local markets, and sausages, although I suppose I could try and make my own. So, yeah, the food. I'd miss the food most. What would I miss least? My mobile – I'd like to be completely un-contactable – at least for a little while.

**Post 3          Paola, Italy**

I would miss the company of people because I know I'd like to have someone to share experiences with. For instance, if there was a fantastic sunrise I'd want someone to be there to enjoy it with me. I'm a sociable sort of person and I'd go mad on my own. And I definitely wouldn't miss junk mail – I hate coming home every evening and finding a pile of junk mail in my post box.

**Post 4          Miko, Japan**

Hi,
I would miss Manga cartoons, the Internet and Japanese food, like nori, sushi and Japanese beef. I'd also miss TV shows and shopping for clothes … and my two dogs. In fact, I'd miss everything.

**Post 5          Roger, UK**

I would miss my daily newspaper and listening to the news on the TV and radio. I'd feel very cut off if I didn't know what was happening in the world. If you gave me a radio, then I'd be perfectly happy to live on a desert island for the rest of my life. What I'd miss least would be traffic jams in the city, particularly my journey to work.

**Post 6          Jayne, Canada**

Why hasn't anyone mentioned their family? I'd be lost without my husband and two kids. They're the most important things for me. Maybe coffee too. I can't get started in the morning without a cup of black coffee. I wouldn't miss doing the housework. Just think, no more cleaning or washing up! And it'd be good to be able to relax as much as I wanted.

**Post 7          Jaime, Mexico**

It would have to be music. I couldn't live without my music! I wouldn't miss going to school at all or doing homework!

## Real life
### Saying numbers

**13** a **T9.6** Listen and circle the number you hear. Then listen again and repeat the numbers.

1  16% / 60%
2  15,025 / 50,025
3  1.5 million / 1.5 billion
4  13°C / 30°C
5  1,045 km² / 1,450 km²
6  a profit of 20% / a profit of 21%

b  Write the numbers in full.

1  47%  _forty-seven per cent_
2  $12,265 _____
3  15 m² _____
4  €305,000 _____
5  30°C _____
6  70 km / hr _____
7  10,000,000 _____
8  4.3 _____

## Pronunciation
### /ʌ/

> **LOOK!**
> The sound /ʌ/ can be spelt in different ways:
> done      lunch      tough
> /ʌ/        /ʌ/          /ʌ/

**14** a  Underline nine words in the box which contain /ʌ/.

| public | stomach | burn | luxury | cough | rough |
|--------|---------|------|--------|-------|-------|
| through | money | woman | push | enough | |
| budget | tongue | encourage | huge | | |

b  **T9.7** Listen to the words and repeat them.

c  Complete the sentences with the words in the box.

1  There's a ____public____ telephone over there.
2  Have you had _____ cake?
3  Ow! I've bitten my _____ !
4  She tried to _____ me to apply for the job.
5  Don't go swimming today – the sea's too _____ .
6  Ian hit me in the _____ .

7  Could you lend me some _____ ?
8  Many years ago, chocolate used to be a _____ .
9  Has your department planned its _____ for next year?

## Vocabulary booster
### Money

**15** a  Put the expressions with money in the columns below. Which two words don't belong in either column?

£ $ € £ $ € £ $ € £ $ €
borrow      earn       give away    inherit
invest      lend       lose         money
save        spend      steal        take
waste       win
£ $ € £ $ € £ $ € £ $ € £

| money comes to you | money goes from you |
|--------------------|---------------------|
| _borrow_ | |
| | |

b  Choose the best answer: a, b or c.

1  Why do you buy lottery tickets? You're _____ your money.
   a  spending   b  giving away   (c  wasting)

2  Could you _____ me €20 until tomorrow?
   a  borrow   b  lend   c  take

3  Bill Gates _____ a lot of money to charity.
   a  gives away   b  saves   c  invests

4  Christine Onassis _____ a fortune from her father.
   a  earned   b  took   c  inherited

5  I _____ my wallet on the train.
   a  lost   b  stole   c  wasted

6  Could I possibly _____ $3,000 from the bank?
   a  lend   b  invest   c  borrow

7  She used to be wealthy but she _____ most of her money in dot com companies in the 1990s.
   a  invested   b  lost   c  wasted

8  The thief _____ a diamond ring worth €8,000.
   a  spent   b  stole   c  gave away

9  The Director _____ twenty times as much as the teachers.
   a  wins   b  takes   c  earns

# Improve your writing
## Opening a bank account

If you go to stay in an English-speaking country for more than a few
months you may want to open a bank account.

---

## Application to open a current account
PLEASE COMPLETE IN BLOCK CAPITALS

Title: ............  Surname: ....................................................................

First name(s): ..............................................................

Date of birth: ...........................

Nationality: ..................................................................

Address: ...........................................................................

...........................................................................

...........................................................................

Postcode ...................................

Tel: Home no. ................................  Work no. ...........................

Marital status: ..........................  Number of dependent children: .........

Where do you live?  With parents ❑  Alone ❑

With partner ❑  Other ❑

Previous address: ...................................................................

...........................................................................

...........................................................................

Postcode ...................................

When did you move to your current address?

Month ....................  Year ....................

What type of other bank or building society accounts do you hold?

Current ❑  Savings/Deposit ❑  Other ❑

How many of each of the following payment cards do you have?

Credit card ❑  Store cards ❑  Debit cards ❑

Employment status (e.g. full-time / part-time / student): ....................

Job title (e.g. Sales assistant): ..............................................

Employer's name and address / Place of study: ...........................

...........................................................................

...........................................................................

Postcode ...................................

When did you start working for your current employer / start your

course of studies?  Month ....................  Year ....................

Mother's maiden name: ...............................................................

*(This personal information may be required as identification for security measures only.)*

Signature ...........................................................................

Date .........................................

---

**16** **a** Look at the vocabulary from the application form and match each word or phrase (1–9) with a definition/example (a–i).

1 title
2 marital status
3 mother's maiden name
4 current account
5 deposit account
6 postcode
7 store card
8 credit card
9 debit card

a single – married – divorced
b You can use this card to buy something and pay at the end of the month.
c You use this account for saving.
d Your mother's surname before she was married.
e Mrs – Mr – Ms – Miss
f You can use this card to buy things at a particular shop, e.g. a department store.
g You can take money from this account whenever you like.
h You can use this card in the same way as a cheque. The money is taken directly from your bank account.
i SE4 2NP (this shows the area that you live in).

**b** You have come to the UK for a year. Decide whether you have come to:

• work for FBT Inc. as a trainee manager. The company's office is at: 7 Grosvenor Place, London WC1 2RP.
• take an English course. The address of the school is: International English, 40 Baker Street, London NW1.

You have rented a flat at this address: Flat 3, 2 Croxted Road, London SE14 2PQ. Phone number: 0208 629 4731. Complete the bank application form and ask your teacher to check it.

## Vocabulary
### Types of story

**1** People were asked 'What book are you going to take on holiday this year?' Complete what they said. The words are from Vocabulary and speaking on page 102 of the Students' Book.

a  *Jurassic Park, Timeline,* anything by Michael Crichton. I know the plots are u _n_ _r_ _e_ _a_ _l_ _i_ _s_ _t_ _i_ _c_, but who cares?

b  An Agatha Christie book. Ten people in an old house, one gets killed. Great! There's nothing better than an old-fashioned c _ _ _ _ story.

c  The latest Harry Potter book. The plots are good and the stories are extremely i _ _ _ _ _ _ _ _ _ _ .

d  I like Patricia Cornwell. I know her books are quite violent, but the plots are very c _ _ _ _ _ _ .

e  I'm going to Romania and there's an old l _ _ _ _ _ that Count Dracula lived in a castle nearby, so I'm going to re-read *Dracula*.

f  I'm going to try *War and Peace*. I started it once but I found all the different characters very c _ _ _ _ _ _ _ _ _ _ and I couldn't follow the story.

g  *Love in the Time of Cholera* by Gabriel García Márquez. I love the characters and the h _ _ _ _ e _ _ _ _ _ _ .

h  Anything by Terry Pratchett. His *Diskworld* series is set in a whole new world and I think he's one of the best f _ _ _ _ _ _ writers ever.

i  Nelson Mandela's autobiography, *Long Walk to Freedom*. I've read it several times and I find it very m _ _ _ _ _ .

j  A good d _ _ _ _ _ _ _ _ story, maybe a Sherlock Holmes story. You know, something with a murder or two and an interesting main character.

k  I like poetry. I've just bought Ted Hughes' *Tales from Ovid*, which are poems about the old Greek m _ _ _ _ .

l  I'm taking my little daughter and so I think a book of f _ _ _ _ t _ _ _ _ , you know, *Sleeping Beauty, Snow White and the Seven Dwarves*, something traditional, with pictures.

m  I'd like something that makes me think, something with a m _ _ _ _ .

n  A good old r_ _ _ _ _ _ , you know the sort of thing: beautiful young girl, good looking, powerful man and it takes them the 400 pages to get together. Just the sort of thing for a holiday read!

# Listen and read
## The world's funniest jokes

2  The University of Hertfordshire conducted research to find the funniest jokes in the world. 350,000 people visited a special site to submit jokes and to vote for their favourite. Here are some of the results of the year-long experiment.

**T10.1**  Listen to and/or read the jokes and match them with the pictures.

### The top joke in the UK
A woman gets on a bus with her baby. The bus driver says, 'That's the ugliest baby I've ever seen!' The woman is furious. She says to a man sitting next to her, 'The driver was extremely rude to me.' The man says, 'Go and speak to him. Go ahead, I'll hold your monkey for you.'

### The top joke in Germany
A general noticed one of his soldiers behaving strangely. The soldier used to pick up every piece of paper that he saw, look at it, and say, 'That's not it.' This went on for some time until the general arranged for a psychologist to see the man. The psychologist decided that the man was crazy and wrote a letter to say he should leave the army. The soldier picked it up, smiled and said, 'That's it!'

### The top joke in Northern Ireland
A doctor says to his patient, 'I have bad news and worse news.' 'Oh dear, what's the bad news?' asks the patient. The doctor replies, 'You only have twenty-four hours to live.' 'That's terrible,' says the patient. 'How can the news possibly be worse?' The doctor replies, 'I've been trying to contact you since yesterday.'

### The top joke in Canada
When the space organisation NASA first started sending up astronauts they discovered ballpoint pens would not work in zero gravity. To solve the problem, NASA scientists spent ten years and $12 billion to develop a pen that would write in zero gravity, upside down, under water, on all types of surface, and at temperatures ranging from below freezing to 300°C. The Russians used a pencil.

### The top joke in the World
Two New Jersey hunters are out in the woods when one of them falls down. He doesn't seem to be breathing and he looks very white. The other man takes out his phone and calls the emergency services. 'My friend is dead! What can I do?' The operator says, 'Calm down. I can help. First go and make sure he is dead.' There is a silence, then a shot is heard. Back on the phone, the man says, 'OK, what next?'

# Pronunciation
## Sentence stress

3  a  **T10.2**  Listen again to the first joke in exercise 2. Underline the stressed words.

A <u>woman</u> gets on a <u>bus</u> with her <u>baby</u>. The bus driver says, 'That's the ugliest baby I've ever seen!' The woman is furious. She says to a man sitting next to her, 'The driver was extremely rude to me.' The man says, 'Go and speak to him. Go ahead, I'll hold your monkey for you.'

b  Practise telling the joke, paying attention to the stress.

# Past perfect

**4** Complete the sentence with the correct Past perfect form of the verbs in the box.

| do | ~~finish~~ | forget | have | leave |
|----|----------|--------|------|-------|
| make | meet | sell | travel | won |

a  He asked why I _hadn't finished_ the reports.

b  There was no coffee because Mark _____ to buy any.

c  Glenn knew he _____ a lot of mistakes in his English exam.

d  I phoned about the car for sale but the owner _____ already _____ it.

e  The children were very hungry because they _____ any breakfast.

f  I was certain I _____ the keys on my desk, but they weren't there.

g  Diana was sure she _____ Tony before.

h  The children _____ by plane before so they were very excited.

i  Mrs Dunn was angry because most of the students _____ their homework.

j  United's manager resigned because the team _____ any matches that season.

# Past perfect or Past simple

**5** Complete the sentences with the best form of the verb in brackets. (In each sentence one verb should be in the Past perfect and the other(s) in the Past simple.)

a  As soon as the film ___started___ (start) Beth realised she ___'d seen___ (see) it before.

b  I _____ (be) surprised to find that Mr Cole _____ (leave) the day before.

c  Helen _____ (feel) much better after she _____ (have) a good sleep.

d  The rain _____ (stop) by the time we _____ (get) to the beach.

e  Melissa _____ (be) angry because her brother _____ (eat) all the chocolates.

f  When Julia _____ (married) Scott she _____ (not realise) he _____ (be married) before.

g  Geoff _____ (not see) his parents for fifteen years so he _____ (feel) rather nervous at the airport.

h  The jazz singer _____ (sing) an old blues song that I _____ (never hear) before.

i  When I _____ (write) the letter I _____ (post) it straightaway.

j  After Sarah _____ (know) Alan for a few weeks he _____ (ask) her out to dinner.

# Present perfect or Past perfect

**6** a  Tick the correct ending for the sentences.

1  Greg felt terrified because …
   a  he's never flown before.
   b  he'd never flown before. ✓

2  How's Susan?
   a  I haven't seen her for ages.
   b  I hadn't seen her for ages.

3  The group *Just Girls* are breaking up and …
   a  they've only been together for three months.
   b  they'd only been together for three months.

4  We were all very tired because …
   a  we've just travelled back from Florida.
   b  we'd just travelled back from Florida.

5  I love eating here. It's the best restaurant …
   a  I've ever been to.
   b  I'd ever been to.

6  The whole country was in shock because …
   a  the President has died.
   b  the President had died.

7  It was the first time Juventus …
   a  have lost a match.
   b  had lost a match.

8  What's the matter?
   a  You've been depressed all week.
   b  You'd been depressed all week.

b  Complete the sentences with your own ideas. Use either the Present perfect or the Past perfect.

1  This is the best meal _____.

2  It was the first time _____.

3  Dave was surprised because _____ _____.

4  I'm not very hungry because _____ _____.

5  Sue played really badly because _____ _____.

## Vocabulary booster
### Criminals and crimes

**7** a Match the criminals in the box to the definitions.

| | | | | |
|---|---|---|---|---|
| arsonist | burglar | fraudster | hijacker | kidnapper |
| mugger | murderer | robber | shoplifter | ~~thief~~ |

1 the general word for a person who steals ___*thief*___

2 a person who steals from people or places
_____

3 a person who breaks into a house and steals
_____

4 a person who steals from shops when they are open _____

5 a person who attacks someone in the street and steals from them _____

6 a person who starts fires _____

7 a person who kills someone (not by accident)
_____

8 a person who takes someone and asks for money from their family _____

9 a person who takes control of an aeroplane, vehicle or ship illegally _____

10 a person who deceives people to get money
_____

b Complete the table.

| | Person | Verb | Crime |
|---|---|---|---|
| 1 | burglar | *to burgle* | *burglary* |
| 2 | murderer | | |
| 3 | shoplifter | | |
| 4 | kidnapper | | |
| 5 | fraudster | | |
| 6 | robber | | |
| 7 | mugger | | |
| 8 | thief | | |
| 9 | arsonist | | |
| 10 | hijacker | | |

c **T10.3** Listen and check. Then practise saying the words. Mark the main stress on all the words in the table in exercise 6.

## Vocabulary
### Language of the law

**8** Replace the definitions in bold with a phrase from Reading and vocabulary on page 104 of the Students' Book. The phrase is the number of words in brackets.

a Yesterday Malcolm James appeared **in front of a judge** in central London. (2 words) ___*in court*___

b Two robbers in Buenos Airies **tried** to rob the same bank four times. (1 word) _____

c She was sure someone had **walked behind** her from the station. (1 word) _____

d When Toby Caine was murdered, the police **thought** it was his wife. (1 word) _____

e Two young boys have been **stopped and taken to the police station** for stealing a car. (1 word)

_____

f After the accident Christine was **asked questions** by detectives for three hours. (1 word) _____

g In court Maria Delgada **said she had done the crime.** (2 words) _____

h Joseph Lewis was taken to the police station and was **formally told by the police that he had done the crime.** (1 word) _____

i At the end of a nine-month court case, the judge **decided that** the company **had not done anything wrong.** (2 words) _____

# Reported speech

## 9
**a** Stacy, a single woman from London, first met Sam on the Internet.

Here is some of the information he wrote about himself on the website.

| | |
|---|---|
| **Name** | Sam Boyd |
| **Location** | I live in Los Angeles. |
| **Occupation** | I'm an actor. |
| **Do you have a girlfriend?** | I'm not seeing anyone at the moment. |
| **Previous relationships** | Nothing serious. I've never been married. In 2004 I was engaged to a girl from Florida but we broke up. |
| **Next visit** | I'll be in the UK on business next March. |

Unfortunately, 'Sam Boyd' didn't exist. He was a criminal who already had three 'wives' in different parts of the world. Later Stacy sold her story to a magazine. Complete the gaps in the article.

He told me (1) __his__ name (2) _____ Sam Boyd, but I found out later that his real name is Michael Rackham. He said he (3) _____ in Los Angeles and that he (4) _____ an actor but actually he had never had a job or a permanent address. The worst thing was that he said he (5) _____ anyone and that he (6) _____ married, but the police records showed that he already has three 'wives'; one in Texas, one in Turkey and one in Austria. And as for the woman in Florida he said that he (7) _____ engaged to, we found out later that he was talking about his sister who lives there! He told me he (8) _____ in the UK on business in March. He'll get an unwelcome surprise then. The police will be waiting for him!

**b** `T10.4` Listen and check.

## 10
**a** Complete the sentences with a reported form of the statements.

❝ Fifty-six people have been killed in a train crash. ❞

❝ I practised eight hours every day. ❞

❝ The world is flat. ❞

❝ I've just got married. ❞

❝ Stephen's doing very well at maths. ❞

❝ You can be anything you want to be! ❞

❝ I'm sure I heard somebody in the garden, Inspector. ❞

❝ People in Brazil use the Internet more than anyone. ❞

❝ It'll rain overnight. ❞

1  When I interviewed Mrs Taylor she said that __she__ __was sure she'd heard somebody in the garden__ .

2  On the weather forecast last night they said _____ .

3  Stephen's teacher told us _____ .

4  When I was young my father told me _____ _____ .

5  They said on the news this morning that _____ _____ .

6  600 years ago people thought that _____ _____ .

7  I've just been reading an article in *Computer Monthly* which said that _____ _____ .

8  My ex-boyfriend sent me a letter saying that _____ _____ .

9  Wayne Rider, the new tennis star, said that when he was young _____ _____ .

**b** `T10.5` Listen to some statements and use the prompts to report them.

You hear:

I'm tired. Jack said …

You say:

Jack said he was tired.

## Reported questions

**11** Alessandro has just arrived in London. He wants to improve his English and yesterday he had a interview at a language school. He's telling his friend about the questions he was asked.

**a** Put the words in the reported questions in the correct order.

1 asked / what / She / my / me / was / name
   *She asked me what my name was.*

2 job / me / wanted / She / was / what / know / to
   _____

3 I / She / me / I / in / had / asked / London / when / arrived
   _____

4 lived / wanted / in / She / if / to / I / Rome / know
   _____

5 in / was / I / asked / London / She / where / me / living
   _____

6 'd / long / I / been / me / She / English / learning / how / asked
   _____

7 I / to / wanted / liked / She / if / know / England
   _____

**b** Write the interviewer's original questions.

1 *What's your name?* _____
2 _____
3 _____
4 _____
5 _____
6 _____
7 _____

**12** **a** Clare has just arrived at San Francisco airport where her friend Josh is meeting her. Clare took a long time to go through immigration. Report the questions that she was asked.

1 Where are you from?
   *He asked me where I was from.*

2 Are you here on holiday?
   _____

3 Are you travelling alone?
   _____

4 Did you pack your suitcases yourself?
   _____

5 Have you been to the USA before?
   _____

6 How long will you be in the country?
   _____

7 Do you know anyone in San Francisco?
   _____

8 Where are you going to stay?
   _____

9 How much money do you have with you?
   _____

**b** **T10.6** Listen to the questions and report them.

You hear:                    You say:

Where are you from?          *He asked me where I was from.*

# Wordspot
## *say* and *tell*

> LOOK!
>
> - *I **told** ~~to~~ Fran that I'd be late.*
>   tell + object
> - *I **said** ~~Fran~~ I'd be late.*
>   say without object
> - *I **said to** Fran that I'd be late.*
>   say + to + object

**13** **a** Five of these sentences have mistakes. Find the mistakes and correct them.

1 Sorry, what did you ~~tell~~? *say*
2 The press report said the President had been in an accident.
3 Matthew hasn't told his boss that he's leaving yet.
4 Pat's father said her she should be more polite.
5 Danny told he was going to the USA.
6 Tell to your brother that you're sorry.
7 Mr Stuart said a lot about the new plans.
8 Could you say me your name again, please.

**b** Circle the correct verb *say* or *tell* and complete the gaps with the words in the box.

| | | | | |
|---|---|---|---|---|
| about | difference | goodbye | ~~joke~~ | no | off |
| sorry | thank you | truth | what | | |

1 Bob *said/(told)* me a good ___*joke*___ about an Englishman, an Irishman and a Scotsman.
2 Her teacher *said/told* Tanya _____ for being late.
3 If a woman asks you 'Do I look fat in this?' never *say/tell* her the _____ !
4 Jo left the party without *saying/telling* _____ .
5 Look I've *said/told* _____ . Can't we just forget about it?
6 Anna's writing a note to her grandparents to *say/tell* _____ for her Christmas present.
7 Could you *say/tell* me _____ your relationship with the President?
8 I asked her if she would go out with me but she *said/told* _____ .
9 Can you *say/tell* me the _____ between the Canadian and American accent?
10 The girl at the Helpdesk was great. I explained the problem and she *said/told* me _____ to do.

# Vocabulary
## Adverbs for telling stories

**14** Complete the sentences from an e-mail about moving to Russia with the adverbs in the box.

| | | | |
|---|---|---|---|
| eventually | fortunately | gradually | ~~immediately~~ |
| obviously | suddenly | surprisingly | unfortunately |

As soon as I got to St Petersburg, I (a) *immediately* fell in the love with the city.

I had some problems getting around at first, but (b) _____ the people are very kind and helped me when I got lost on the Metro.

I've started Russian lessons and my speaking is (c) _____ improving.

The weather's been brilliant. (d) _____ , there had been no snow until November this year (usually it starts in October).

Last Tuesday it (e) _____ started snowing in the middle of the afternoon at work and it hasn't stopped since then.

My apartment is small but clean and not too expensive. (f) _____ it's a long way from the office and I missed the last Metro home last night.

I was waiting for a taxi when a man came up to me and started talking to me very loudly. I think he'd been drinking and (g) _____ I felt quite frightened.

A young man came and helped me. He waited with me until (h) _____ a taxi arrived.

## Improve your writing
### Checking for mistakes

**15** Here is a Japanese legend written by a student. The teacher has marked the mistakes using the following code. Look at the code and correct the mistakes.

^ for a missing word     sp for spelling     wo for word order     vf for verb form     ww for a wrong word

# Tsuru no On-gaeshi: The Crane

Once there was *a* /poor hunter who lived in Japan. One day he was hunting    ^

and he find a crane caught in a tree. He felt sorry for the crane and he freed    vf

it. Than he went home and forgot about it.    ww

A few days later, a lovely woman came to the hunter's house. They felt in    ww

love and they got married. His wife new was kind and beautiful but he didn't    wo

have enugh money for two people. She saw his problems and offered to    sp

weave some fabric so that he could sell it in the market – but she said him    ww

that he must never watch her.

She stayed in the weaving hut during three days. At last she came out with a    ww

beuatiful fabric called Tsuru-no-senba-ori (thousand feathers of a crane). The    sp

hunter sold the fabric for a lot gold. The hunter quickly spent all the gold    ^

and he asked her several times to make fabric more. The hunter became richer    wo

and richer but his wife gradually became thiner and thiner.    sp (x2)

Eventually, she said that she can not work because she was too tired. But her    vf

husband was greedy and asked her to weave the fabric once longer. Three days    ww

passed, then four, then five, but she not did come out of the hut. In the end, on the    wo

sixth morning, hunter was so worried that he finally looked through the window    ^

of the hut. To his surprising, it was not a woman but a crane that was weaving.    ww

Finally, his wife came out from the weaving hut with the fabric in arms. She    ^

said, 'You have seen my true appearance, so I not can stay with you any longer.'    wo

Then she changed into a crane and fly away.    vf

## Obligation and permission

**1** Rewrite the sentences replacing the words in bold with the correct form of *is/are allowed to*.

a You **can't** smoke here.
  *You aren't allowed to smoke here.*

b You **can** walk on the grass.
  _____

c **Is it okay for us** to use a calculator?
  _____

d Visitors **must not** touch the exhibits.
  _____

e On Saturdays we **can** stay up until ten o'clock.
  _____

f Children under five **cannot** use the swimming pool without an adult.
  _____

g **Can I** hang pictures on the walls?
  _____

**2** **a** Complete the sentences with the words in the box.

| | | | | | |
|---|---|---|---|---|---|
| should | shouldn't | can | can't | must | mustn't |
| ought | ~~have~~ | don't have | are allowed | | |
| aren't allowed | | | | | |

1 You ___*have*___ to leave your keys at reception when you go out of the hotel.

2 I think people _____ spend more time with their families and less time at work.

3 Passengers _____ to walk around the plane when it is taking off.

4 Candidates _____ to take a dictionary into the exam, but they can't take in a grammar book.

5 You _____ buy alcohol in a pub unless you're over eighteen.

6 You look really tired. I think you _____ to take a day off.

7 Monday's a holiday so we _____ to go to school until Tuesday.

8 You _____ ride a bicycle on the motorway – it's very dangerous.

9 Guests _____ have breakfast any time between 7.00 and 9.00 a.m.

10 I know I _____ really smoke so much, but it helps me to relax.

11 You _____ sign your name in this book when you enter or leave the building.

**b** **T11.1** Listen and check. Then practise saying the sentences, paying attention to the weak forms.

**3** Here are the answers to some questions about rules. First decide if they are about a language class (LC), a library (LIB) or a sports club (SC). Then use the prompts to make complete questions.

a You can borrow four books at a time. ___LIB___
  How many books / allowed / borrow / at a time?
  *How many books am I allowed to borrow at a time* ?

b Yes, you can book two days in advance. _____
  Can / book / aerobics classes in advance?
  _____ ?

c You're allowed to keep them for a week. _____
  How long / allowed / keep books?
  _____ ?

d Yes, first you take a short written test, then there's an interview with a teacher. _____
  Have to / take a test?
  _____ ?

e Yes, bring a passport-sized photo for your membership card. _____
  Should / bring a photo?
  _____ ?

f Well, if you miss too many, you won't get a certificate at the end of the course. _____
  _____ ?
  How many classes / allowed / miss?
  _____ ?

## Short answers

**4** Complete the short answers.

a  Can I pay now?

Yes, ___*you can*___ . How would you like to pay?

b  Does Alan have to wear a school uniform?

No, _____ . For the first year children wear their normal clothes.

c  Am I allowed to take photos?

I think _____ . It doesn't say you can't.

d  Can I watch the football?

No, _____ . It's your bedtime.

e  Should I bow when I meet the director?

I think _____ . It's the custom here.

f  Do I have to take the medicine?

Yes, _____ if you want to get better.

## Vocabulary
### Rules

**5** Complete the rules about driving with the words in the box.

| crossings | ~~driving test~~ | fine | lorries | motorways |
| park | seat belt | | | |

a  You aren't allowed to drive until you've passed your ___*driving test*___ .

b  You have to wear a _____ .

c  You often have to pay to _____ your car in the city centre.

d  You always have to stop at pedestrian _____ .

e  It's an offence to drive faster than 110 kph on British _____ .

f  You usually have to pay a _____ if you are caught driving too fast.

g  _____ can't drive into the city centre between 9 a.m. and 5 p.m.

## Obligation and permission in the past

**6** Paolo has just finished his military service abroad and is talking about the rules and regulations in the army. Change his sentences to the past.

a  I have to get up at 5.30 a.m.
   ___*I had to get up at 5.30 a.m.*___

b  I must clean my boots every day.
   _____

c  I'm not allowed to have long hair.
   _____

d  I can't e-mail home.
   _____

e  We can watch a movie every Saturday evening.
   _____
   _____

f  We are allowed go into town once a month.
   _____
   _____

g  I don't have to pay for my meals.
   _____

**7** Reorder the words in these conversations. The first word is underlined.

**a**  KIM AND PIETER ARE TALKING ABOUT A MATHS EXAM.

KIM:  exam / to / calculator / <u>Were</u> / a / allowed / the / take / into / you ?

(1) ___*Were you allowed to take a calculator*___
    ___*into the exam?*___

PIETER:  weren't / <u>No</u> / we

(2) _____

KIM:  did / answer / many / have / <u>How</u> / questions / to / you ?

(3) _____
    _____

PIETER:  three / <u>We</u> / do / in / had / hours / twenty / to

(4) _____
    _____

**b** PATRIZIA AND ITALO ARE TALKING ABOUT A SUMMER CAMP.

PATRIZIA: up / allowed / you / late / to / <u>Were</u> / stay ?

(1) _____

_____

ITALO: campfire / we / by / midnight / <u>Yeah</u> / until / sit / the / could

(2) _____

_____

PATRIZIA: get / early / you / up / <u>Did</u> / to / have ?

(3) _____

ITALO: to / nine / we / <u>No</u> / up / didn't / until / get / have

(4) _____

_____

**c** MONA IS TALKING TO VANESSA ABOUT VANESSA'S DAUGHTER, FRANCOISE.

MONA: America / a / Did / have / Francoise / time / in / good ?

(1) _____

_____

VANESSA: six / week / to / she / work / No / a / days / had

(2) _____

_____

MONA: terrible / That's !

(3) _____

_____

VANESSA: allowed / us / to / wasn't / she / phone / And

(4) _____

_____

**8** These people are talking about their lives when they were ten. Change the sentences (if necessary) so that they are true for you.

a  MARIA: I had to wear white gloves and a hat to school.

*I didn't have to wear gloves or a hat.*

b  JOHN: I couldn't stay up after 8.00 p.m. during the week.

_____

_____

c  LISBETH: We were allowed to wear whatever we wanted at school.

_____

d  ANNA: I could go out to play with my friends whenever I wanted to.

_____

_____

e  JANE: We weren't allowed to speak in the corridors at school.

_____

_____

f  JUDIT: We could call our teachers by their first names.

_____

_____

## *must* and *have to*

**9** Complete the sentences with the words in the box.

| must    mustn't (x2)    have to    don't have to (x2) |
| had to    didn't have to |

a  You ___*mustn't*___ smoke in the library.

b  It's free to get in: you _____ pay.

c  I missed my train and I _____ wait half an hour for the next one.

d  It's not a direct flight to New Zealand: you _____ change planes at Bangkok.

e  There were only two people in front of me in the queue so I _____ wait long.

f  Don't cry, Jessica – you _____ play with Jon if you don't want to.

g  You _____ walk on the railway line.

h  I _____ remember to post this letter.

## Vocabulary
### Expressing opinions

**10** a Use the prompts to make full sentences.

1 It should / illegal / drop rubbish on the streets
*It should be illegal to drop rubbish on the streets.*

2 Take / photographs / famous people on holiday / should / banned

_____

_____ .

3 Young people should / have / right / watch any film they want

_____

_____ .

4 People should / sent / prison / copy videos illegally

_____

_____ .

5 People should / fined / eat on public transport

_____

_____ .

6 It should / against / law / women over 60 / have babies

_____

_____ .

b For each of the opinions above, what do people think? Complete the words. The words come from page 116 of the Students' Book.

1 It's s e n s i b l e .
2 It's f _ i _ .
3 It's too l _ b _ r _ _ _ .
4 It's too h _ r _ h.
5 It's r _ d _ c _ l _ _ _ s.
6 It's u _ f _ _ _ r.

## Vocabulary booster
### Accidents, injuries and illnesses

**11** a Which of the words in bold below can you see in the pictures?

**A**

1 ☑ You could get a **lump**
2 ☐ You could **get a black eye**
3 ☐ You could **burn** yourself
4 ☐ It could become **swollen**
5 ☐ You could start **sneezing**
6 ☐ You might break your ankle
7 ☐ You might fall over
8 ☐ You might get a **blister**
9 ☐ You might get a **rash**
10 ☐ You might **get indigestion**
11 ☐ You'll probably **feel breathless**
12 ☐ You'll probably **get sunburn**

**B**

a if an insect bites your hand.
b if you get wet on a cold day.
c if you run fast up some stairs.
d if you are allergic to food and you eat it.
e if you get hit in the face.
f if you spill a hot drink on your hand.
g if you spend too long in the sun.
h if you feel dizzy.
i if you eat too fast.
j if you trip over something.
k if you go for a long walk in new shoes.
l if you fall over and hit your head.

b Match the beginnings of the sentences in A with the endings in B.

## Listen and read
## Children sue parents

12 a **T11.2** Listen to and/or read the four newspaper stories about children who have sued their parents. Write a sentence for each story summarising the reason why they sued.

1 *Mario Silva's father threatened him with a gun*
  *after he refused to cut his hair.*

2 _____
  _____

3 _____
  _____

4 _____
  _____

b Listen and/or read again. Which person or people …

1 wanted separation from their parents?
  *Mario, Dominique*

2 did not like the way their child looked?
  _____

3 liked the way their child looked?
  _____

4 had an accident? _____

5 was afraid of one of their parents?
  _____

6 was not in control of their own money?
  _____

7 had a famous son or daughter?
  _____

8 was successful in suing their parents?
  _____

c Match the numbers to the things they refer to.

1 ☐ 5
2 ☐ 1,000
3 ☐ 2
4 ☐ 15
5 ☐ 1996

a the number of years father had been telling child to do something
b the age child was when he sued
c the number of jars of cookies
d the year the child left home
e the amount paid for damages

When fifteen-year-old Mario Silva refused to cut his hair because he wanted to look like his favourite film star, his father pulled out a gun and threatened to shoot him. 'My husband had been telling Mario to get his hair cut for the last two years and they had an argument,' said his wife. Fernando Silva was arrested and will appear in court next week. Meanwhile Mario has decided to sue him and to ask to be formally separated from his parents. 'I don't feel safe in the house anymore,' he told our reporter.

A Jamaican woman sued her parents after falling down the stairs of their home during a visit. Beatrice, who was in her early twenties, said that her parents had been negligent because they 'failed to look after the carpet on the stairs.' As a result of the fall she suffered serious and permanent injuries when she tripped over the carpet in August 2002. She was awarded $1,000 in damages at a court in Kingston.

In 1996, seventeen-year-old Olympic gold medallist Dominique Moceneau left home and asked to become a legal adult and to be in control of her own money. She said that her father, Dumitru Moceneau, had taken all her winnings and left her with no money and that her parents had robbed her of her childhood by pushing her so hard to become a gymnast. After hearing her complaints a Texan court granted her independence from her parents.

A Canadian actress is suing her parents for making her fat. Tina Stowe, a well-known TV star in Canada, says that her mother, Lisa, kept five jars of cookies in the house in places where a child could easily find them and used to make the situation worse by telling her she was prettier than the other girls in her school. Stowe has said that her mother should have married a more suitable partner, preferably someone of a slimmer build. Stowe will appear in court next month.

## Improve your writing
### Linking words

**13** Read the text and circle the correct linking word.

Nowadays science has made it possible for a couple who can't have children to pay a woman to have their baby for them. These 'surrogate' mothers sign a contract promising to give the baby to the couple as soon as it is born, in return for a large sum of money. (a) *However* / *Also*, this business arrangement does not always work well in practice and, (b) *despite this* / *as a result*, there have been a number of 'horror stories' in the newspapers recently.

People have strong feelings on both sides. Some say that it is every woman's right to have a child. (c) *Although* / *What is more*, a surrogate mother can often save an unhappy marriage and make some money for herself. (d) *Therefore* / *Despite this*, many people are against this practice. They say that (e) *although* / *besides* they understand the heartache of a childless woman, having a baby is not an automatic right. They feel the whole thing is completely unnatural and (f) *for this reason* / *also* should not be allowed. (g) *Besides* / *However*, they ask what will happen to the child when he or she is old enough to know the truth. This could have a terrible effect on their mental and emotional development. I feel that this last point is particularly important and, (h) *therefore* / *what is more*, I tend to agree that surrogacy is wrong, or at least that there should be stricter rules about it.

## Wordspot
### *do*

**14** Complete the dialogues with the words in the box.

| | | | | |
|---|---|---|---|---|
| badly | best | homework | ironing | ~~languages~~ |
| overtime | well | yoga | | |

a A: You speak Spanish very well.
  B: Thanks. I did ___languages___ at university.

b A: How were your exam results?
  B: Well, I passed seven, but I did _____ in maths and science.

c A: Do you go to exercise classes?
  B: Well, I do _____ on Tuesdays and aerobics on Thursdays.

d A: Does everybody earn the same amount?
  B: No, workers are paid double if they do _____ .

e A: Can I watch *Robot Wars*?
  B: Only if you do your _____ first.

f A: Did you see that documentary on TV last night?
  B: Yes, I watched it while I did the _____ .

g A: Do the children like their new school?
  B: Yes, I think so. And they're doing _____ .

h A: Can you get us tickets for the Liverpool match?
  B: Well, I'll do my _____ but I can't promise anything.

## Pronunciation
### Compound nouns

**15** Mark the stress on these compound nouns from Module 11. Look back at page 83 of the Students' Book to remind you of the stress patterns.

1  cápital púnishment
2  car park
3  city centre
4  driving test
5  fast food
6  heart disease

7  military service
8  pedestrian crossing
9  seat belt
10  smoking area
11  swimming pool
12  train station

b **T11.3** Listen and check. Then practise saying them.

## could have

**1** Rewrite these sentences so that they mean the same, using *could have*.

a Perhaps Kate's forgotten that we invited her.

*Kate could have forgotten that we invited her.*

b It was possible that Elena ate your sandwich.

Elena _____ .

c Maybe you left your wallet in the bank.

You _____ .

d Jason may have caught an earlier train.

Jason _____ .

## should have

**2** What would you 'say' in these situations? Complete the sentences using *should(n't) have*, and the verb in brackets.

a You left your car in a car park without buying a ticket. You have to pay a €30 fine.

I *should have bought a ticket* _____ . (buy)

b You told your best friend Anna a secret. She told your boyfriend Tom.

You _____ . (tell)

c You've been waiting one hour for a bus because you thought a taxi was too expensive.

We _____ . (take)

d Your colleague has made a decision without discussing something with you first.

You _____ . (discuss)

e Your friend's laptop was stolen from his car.

He _____ . (leave)

## would have

**3** Imagine you are alive 100 years ago. Make sentences about your life, using *would(n't) have*.

a *I wouldn't have had a computer.* _____

b _____

c _____

d _____

e _____

f _____

## could have / should have / would have

**4** Look at the pictures and match them to the captions below.

a ☐ 2 'Oh well, they wouldn't have had room for my luggage, anyway.'

b ☐ 'What do you mean, you gave him your sweets? I'd have hit him.'

c ☐ 'Darling, you could have hurt yourself.'

d ☐ 'Oh well, it's not too bad – we could have lost everything.'

e ☐ 'I knew I shouldn't have gone to that hairdresser.'

f ☐ 'You should have told me your boss was a vegetarian.'

**5** Complete the sentences with a phrase from the box, and the best form of the verb in brackets.

| | | |
|---|---|---|
| could have (x2) | couldn't have | should have (x2) |
| shouldn't have | would have (x2) | wouldn't have |

a  Oh no, I've forgotten Marcel's address. I knew I _should have written_ (write) it down.

b  Why didn't you buy them that picture? I'm sure they _____ (like) it.

c  We did our best to catch the train: we _____ (run) any faster.

d  You _____ (listen) to Paul. You know he has some stupid ideas.

e  I like Kristin's new motorbike, but I _____ (buy) a bigger one.

f  Look where you're going – we were really close to that car. We _____ (have) an accident.

g  You were right not to tell her the truth about Brian: she _____ (believe) you, anyway.

h  Rupert _____ (be) a great pianist, but he didn't practise enough.

i  The room was a terrible mess when the men had finished painting it. I _____ (do) it myself.

**6** **T12.1** Listen to these sentences and repeat what you hear. Circle the correct phrase.

a  *You shouldn't walk / You shouldn't have walked* home so late at night.

b  *We could invite / We could have invited* our teacher to the picnic on Saturday.

c  Do you still have a headache? *You should take / You should have taken* an aspirin.

d  I'm glad you bought a cake. *I wouldn't have / I wouldn't have had* time to make one.

e  Has Jon really gone running in this rain? *I'd stay / I'd have stayed* at home.

f  Mum and I waited for nearly an hour. *We couldn't wait / We couldn't have waited* any longer.

## Vocabulary
## Collocations

**7** **a** Cross out the collocation which isn't correct. The collocations come from Language focus 1 on pages 122 and 123 (see also the tapescript on page 000) of the Students' Book.

| 1 | make
support
~~do~~ | a decision |
|---|---|---|
| 2 | win
make
enter | a competition |
| 3 | 
suffer from | anxiety
loneliness
danger |
| 4 | catch
develop
overcome | a fear of … |
| 5 | to face
to give up
to add to | the danger |
| 6 | to go
to prepare for
complete | a journey |

**b** Complete the sentences with a verb from the collocations above.

1  Have you ever ___won___ a prize in a competition?

2  How would you _____ for a journey around the world?

3  In what situations could you _____ from loneliness?

4  Should you _____ a friend's decision even when you don't agree with him or her?

5  Have you ever _____ a serious danger to your life?

6  Do you have a fear of something? If so, when did the fear _____ ?

## Imaginary situations in the past with *if*

**8** Match the sentence beginnings in A with the endings in B.

**A**

a  [3]  If I hadn't forgotten my passport
b  [ ]  If Sara and I had stayed longer in Paris
c  [ ]  If we'd booked our theatre tickets in advance
d  [ ]  If Greta hadn't bought a new coat
e  [ ]  If Malcolm had stopped smoking
f  [ ]  If my uncle lived near the airport
g  [ ]  If it hadn't rained
h  [ ]  If you hadn't taken so long to get ready

**B**

1  she'd have enough money to pay her rent.
2  I'd have stayed at his house on my way to Germany.
3  I'd be on the plane to Tunisia.
4  we wouldn't have had to queue outside.
5  we could have taken the children to the zoo.
6  we wouldn't have missed our bus.
7  he wouldn't be in hospital now.
8  we'd gone up the Eiffel Tower.

**9** **a** Read the following newspaper article and answer the questions.

1  Why did Prasad run away from home?
2  What did his family think had happened to him?

> The family of an Indian boy who disappeared from home two years ago were amazed to see him on TV receiving a national award.
>
> Prasad Akkonan's relatives had started to think the boy must be dead when they saw him winning the award for being top scorer in his exam.
>
> Prasad ran away from home 'to become something in life' after his family forced him to enrol in an electrician's course against his wishes.
>
> He went to Bombay and then to Nangpur where he worked as a waiter at a tea stall during the day, and studied at night. His family had no idea what had happened to him until they saw him receiving his award for scoring 86.5%, the highest amongst millions of students in his Higher Secondary Exam.

**b** Use the prompts to make full sentences about the story.

1  If / he / not / decide / 'become something in life' / he / not / run away

   *If he hadn't decided to 'become something in life', he wouldn't have run away.*

2  If / he / not / run away / he / do / an electrician's course

   _____

   _____

3  If / he / stay / at home / he / be / an electrician now

   _____

   _____

4  He / not / have / enough money to study / if / he / not / work / as a waiter

   _____

   _____

5  If / he / write / to his parents / they / not / think / he was dead

   _____

   _____

6  If / they / not / see / the programme/ they / still / think / he was dead

   _____

   _____

7  He / not / have / score / 86.5% / if / he / not / work hard

   _____

   _____

8  If / he / not / be / very clever / he / not / won / the award

   _____

   _____

## Vocabulary
### Problems and solutions

 **a** Complete the conversations with the words and phrases in the box. The words are from Vocabulary on page 126 of the Students' Book.

| | |
|---|---|
| come up | expert advice |
| go away | ~~helpdesk~~ ignore |
| sort it out | talk it over |
| make up our minds | concerned |

**1**

A: Jen, can you help me?

B: Sure, what's the problem?

A: This CD player isn't working.

B: *(30 minutes later)* I give up! You should contact the (a) _helpdesk_ and get some (b) _____ .

**2**

A: Hello, David Holden.

B: Hi, David, this is Bill. Look, a problem has (c) _____ and I need to (d) _____ , so I can't meet you for lunch.

**3**

A: Hello, I'm Maria Gonzales. I'm Rosie's mother.

B: Ah Mrs. Gonzales, thank you for coming. I'm feeling rather (e) _____ about Rosie. She seems very depressed at the moment. I thought we could (f) _____ the problem, and hope it would just (g) _____ but yesterday she started fighting with another child and so I wanted to (h) _____ with you to see if there's a problem at home. Then maybe we can (i) _____ what to do.

**b** **T12.2** Listen and check.

## Improve your writing
### A letter to sort out a problem

**11** **a** Lucy Humphries booked a flight to Mexico City and paid by credit card. She received her ticket a few days later, but the dates on the ticket were wrong. She sent the ticket back to the travel agent's, but nearly two weeks have passed and she has not heard from them.

Lucy has written a letter to sort out the problem. Reorder the sentences below.

44 Barn Road
Nottingham NS4
29th May

The Manager Eurotrips Travel Agents

Dear Sir/Madam,

| a | A week later, I received my credit card receipt and the ticket, but unfortunately the dates were wrong. |
|---|---|
| b | That was ten days ago, and I've heard nothing from you since. |
| c | You booked me onto a flight costing €575, which I paid by credit card. |
| d | I look forward to hearing from you. |
| e | As you can imagine, I am very concerned about this because I need to make other arrangements for my trip, which I cannot do until the dates are confirmed. |
| f | Several weeks ago I telephoned your office to book a return flight to Mexico City, leaving on 8th July and returning 27th July. |
| g | I would therefore be grateful if you would look into this matter urgently. |
| h | I immediately returned the ticket by registered post, with a note explaining the problem. |

Yours faithfully,

*L Humphries*

**b** In your notebook write a letter to sort out the problem below. Use the letter above to help you. Show your letter to your teacher.

Three weeks ago, you booked a four-week course at the Success Language School, 354 Liffey Road, Dublin DN6. A week ago, you had not received a receipt or confirmation of your place on the course. You phoned the school and left a message on the answering machine, but you have still not heard anything.

Before you write the letter, decide:
- How many hours a day your course is: 3 / 4 / 5 ?
- How you paid for the course: credit card / bank transfer?
- The dates of your course.

# Vocabulary booster
## Love and relationships

**12** (T12.3) Put the following events in order to tell the story of a relationship. Then listen and check.

a ☐ so we decided to **split up**.

b ☐2 We started talking, liked each other, and we found we **had a lot in common**.

c ☐ However, we **missed** each other a lot

d ☐1 Carole and I met on a training course two years ago.

e ☐ But then I had to go away for three months and we **drifted apart**.

f ☐ and **I'm seeing** someone else.

g ☐ but it didn't **work out**

h ☐3 As we **got to know** each other we **became very close**

i ☐ and in the end we **broke up** again.

j ☐ so we started going out **with each other**.

k ☐ It's taken me six months but now I think I'm **over her**

l ☐ and so we **got back together**,

m ☐ When I came back we started having a lot of arguments

**13** Complete the sentences with the correct form of the phrases from exercise 12.

a I _became very close_ to my mother after I had a baby of my own. I find I can tell her anything now.

b Gina and Doug _____ last week and he's already _____ someone else.

c Luke seems really nice; I'd like to _____ him better.

d My classmate and I have a _____ . We live in the same street and we both love football!

e I thought I was _____ Rodney but I still think about him all the time.

f We met on holiday and everything was wonderful, but when we went home we didn't write or phone much and we just _____ .

g Duncan and Rachel got married a year ago, but it didn't _____ and they've just got divorced.

# Pronunciation
## Difficult words

**14** a Match the words in A with their pronunciation in B.

| A | | B | |
|---|---|---|---|
| 1 | anxiety | a | /ˌɒpəˈtjuːnɪti/ |
| 2 | toughest | b | /ˈfɪzɪkəl/ |
| 3 | physical | c | /rɪˈleɪʃənʃɪp/ |
| 4 | phobia | d | /ˈtʌfəst/ |
| 5 | rescued | e | /æŋˈzaɪəti/ |
| 6 | fulfil | f | /ˌɑːgjʊˈmentətɪv/ |
| 7 | ambition | g | /fʊlˈfɪl/ |
| 8 | expert | h | /ˈekspɜːt/ |
| 9 | bruised | i | /æmˈbɪʃən/ |
| 10 | opportunity | j | /səˈlɪsətə/ |
| 11 | solicitor | k | /ˈɑːgjʊment/ |
| 12 | relationship | l | /bruːzd/ |
| 13 | argument | m | /ˈreskjuːd/ |
| 14 | argumentative | n | /ˈfəʊbiə/ |

b (T12.4) Listen and repeat.

# Wordspot
## *think*

**15** Complete the sentences with the words in the box.

| | | | | | | |
|---|---|---|---|---|---|---|
| back | just | myself | of | ~~of~~ | over | should |
| so | straight | the | world | up | | |

a What do you think ___of___ of my new hairstyle?

b Stella's appearing on TV. _____ think! She could be famous!

c We need to think _____ a name for the new range of cosmetics.

d We've thought it _____ and we've decided to offer the job to Thomas Ferrier.

e Is Pukhet in Malaysia? I don't think _____ .

f I _____ think it'll cost about $200.

g You know I think _____ of my father!

h I'm so tired I can't think _____ .

i We're thinking _____ moving to Mexico.

j My mother always taught me to think for _____ .

k I often think _____ to my schooldays.

## Listen and read
## The greatest romantic films of all time?

Boy meets girl. Boy falls in love with girl. Boy gets girl. The recipe for a romance? Maybe not, if we look at the three top romantic films of all time, according to a recent vote by filmgoers. It seems that the films we remember best are those ones where love doesn't always have a happy ending.

**16** a  **T12.5**  Listen to and/or read the text about three films and match each to its title.

1  Doctor Zhivago
2  Casablanca
3  Titanic

**A** _____

One of the most beloved of American films, this is a classic story of a love triangle between two men and one woman. It is the story of Rick Blaine (Humphrey Bogart) who runs a nightclub in a town in Morocco during World War II. Rick's café has become a place where people can get illegal papers to help them to escape from Europe to America. One day, to Rick's horror, Ilsa (Ingrid Bergman) walks through the door of his café ('Of all the gin joints in all the towns in all the world, she walks into mine'). Rick and Ilsa were lovers in Paris before the war but he thinks that she left him. Their romantic feelings soon return but Rick and Ilsa must face a painful choice, should Ilsa go to America with her husband, Victor (an important war hero who needs her support) or should she stay with Rick, the love of her life? In the end Bogart makes the decision for her and does the hardest thing for any man in love. He lets her go. In one of the most famous goodbye scenes ever recorded on film, he wipes away her tears and says: 'Here's looking at you kid.'

**B** _____

The romance in this film is tragic because it is so intense and lasts for such a short time. And because it is only a small part of a terrible and huge drama. A voyage on a ship going to New York brings together Rose, a high-class seventeen-year-old girl, and a third-class passenger. Everyone who has seen this movie remembers Kate Winslet and Leonardo Di Caprio together at the bow of the ship, the wind blowing in their hair and their hearts full of hope ('Jack, I'm flying!'). She thinks her biggest problem is to decide whether to marry her rich fiancé or to leave him for her new love. We know that in the next three hours they will both face terrible danger and that he will have to die so that she can live.

**C** _____

The music is unforgettable, the photography is extraordinary and the romance is moving. Against the background of the Russian Revolution, this is the story of a doctor who is in love with two women, one of them his wife and the other his lover (Lara). Omar Sharif and Julie Christie play the lovers who are separated and then brought back together again by war and destiny. Everyone suffers in this powerful but tiny human story and also in the bigger story of the events of the Revolution. The film is about the choices people have to make between love and duty to their family and to their country. Eventually Lara and the doctor decide to part but the ending is not completely sad. Many years later we see that their daughter has survived and the future for her looks more hopeful.

b  **Listen and/or read again and answer the questions.**

1  Where does each film take place?
   A  _____
   B  _____
   C  _____

2  Each film is about three people. Who are they?
   A  _____
   B  _____
   C  _____

3  Is the ending happy or sad or both?
   A  _____
   B  _____
   C  _____

# Real life
## Starting and finishing conversations

**17** **a** Match the speech bubbles to make complete phrases for starting and finishing conversations.

1 [f] Hello, I've heard     a getting here?

2 [ ] It's getting …        b the time?

3 [ ] I'm sorry to interrupt but I have to   c go now.

4 [ ] How are you? I haven't   d must rush.

5 [ ] Hi, glad you           e in Prague.

6 [ ] Did you have any problems   f a lot about you.

7 [ ] Oh, dear, is that      g could come.

8 [ ] I really               h late.

9 [ ] I hear you're going to study   i seen you for ages.

**b** Now write the complete phrases in the correct column of the table.

| Starting conversations | Finishing conversations |
|---|---|
| Hello, I've heard a lot about you. | |
| | |
| | |
| | |

**c** Look at the following situations which take place at a party. Choose the best phrase (1–9 from above) for each situation.

1 You're having a party. The doorbell rings, you open the door and see two good friends. What do you say?

   _Hi, glad you could come._

2 It's a cold night and there's ice on the roads. You know your friends came by car. As you take their coats, what do you ask?

   _____

3 As you go into the party, your friend Simon comes up and sees your guests. It's a long time since he has seen them. What does he say?

   _____
   _____

4 You take your friends into the party and introduce them to your sister. What does your sister say?

   _____
   _____

5 Later at the party, one of your guests introduces his girlfriend to you. You don't know very much about her, except that she's going to study in Prague. What do you say?

   _____
   _____

6 It's 11.30. You're in the middle of a conversation and a friend who lives a long way away comes up to you. What does he say?

   _____
   _____

7 It's one o'clock. You've been having a very interesting conversation with one of your guests when she suddenly looks at her watch. What does she say? (Two phrases together)

   _____
   _____

**d** **T12.6** Listen to the situations and say the correct phrase.

You hear:

   You're having a party. The doorbell rings, you open the door and see two good friends.

You say:

   Hi, glad you could come.

**Pearson Education Limited**
Edinburgh Gate
Harlow
Essex CM20 2JE
England
and Associated Companies throughout the world.

www.longman.com

First published 2005
Second impression 2005

ISBN-10: 0-582-82519-9
ISBN-13: 978-0-582-82519-2

Set in 9pt Stone Informal

Printed in Malaysia

Designed by Jenny Coles

Project Managed by Lindsay White

**Author Acknowledgements**

The publishers and authors would like to thank the following people for their help and contribution: Sarah Cunningham and Peter Moor for their ongoing encouragement and advice; Jonathan Tennant and all at International House Sydney for their encouragement and support; Bill Eales and our colleagues at International House London for their support; Jonathan Barnard, Jenny Coles, Jenny Colley, Yolanda Durham, Alma Gray, Tina Gulyas, Liz Moore, Sarah Munday, Ann Oakley, Shona Rodger, Lindsay White.

The publishers and authors are very grateful to the following people for reporting on the manuscript: Amanda Bailey, St. Giles School of English, London; Leslie Hendra, International House, London.

We are grateful to the following for permission to reproduce copyright material:
Excerpts of Customer Reviews Ananova Limited for an extract adapted from "Missing Indian boy spotted on TV winning exams award" published at www.ananova.com; Amazon.com, Inc. All rights reserved. Used with permission; British Sky Broadcasting Limited for an extract adapted from "Johnny Depp" published at www.skymovies.com; Matt Connolly for extracts from www.iusedtobelieve.com; Discover The World for an extract adapted from "Lapland Adventure Weekend" published at www.artic-experience.co.uk; and Pearson Education Limited for extracts from the *Longman Dictionary of Contemporary English*.

In some instances we have been unable to trace the owners of copyright material and we would appreciate any information that would enable us to do so.

**Photo Acknowledgements**

We are grateful to the following for permission to reproduce copyright photographs:
Alamy/Carol Dixon for page 27 (bottom); Ambient Imates Inc/Peter Bennett for page 28 (top); John Birdsall for page 40 (bottom), 41 top; Corbis/Aero Graphics Inc for page 26; Stephen Frink for page 27 (top); Education Photos/John Walmsley for page 40 (top); Getty Images/Stone/John Lawrence for page 28 (bottom); Leland Bobbe for page 72; Greg Evans International for page 88; Rex Features/Vinnie Zuffante for page 34; Time Newspapers for page 35; Zefa/Masterfile for page 31; Masterfile/Rick Gomez for page 41 (bottom).

Illustrated by Kathy Baxendale, Colin Brown, Joan Corlass, Nicky Dupays, Stephanie Hawken, Conny Jude, Tim Kahane, Aziz Khan, Ian Mitchell, Nicky Taylor and Teresa Tibberts.

Cover photo © Getty Images/Image Bank.